YOUTH VIOLENCE PREVENTION: A SOURCEBOOK FOR COMMUNITY ACTION

YOUTH VIOLENCE PREVENTION: A SOURCEBOOK FOR COMMUNITY ACTION

T.N. THORNTON
C.A. CRAF
L.L. DAHLBERG
B.S. LYNCH
AND
K. BAER

Novinka Books
New York

For permission to use material from this book please contact us:
Telephone 631-231-7269; Fax 631-231-8175
Web Site: http://www.novapublishers.com

NOTICE TO THE READER

LIBRARY OF CONGRESS CATALOGING-IN-PUBLICATION DATA
Available upon request

ISBN 1-59454-705-X

Published by Nova Science Publishers, Inc. ✢ *New York*

CONTENTS

PREFACE

We see it on the nightly news, read about it in the newspaper, hear about it from our children, and witness it firsthand—young people getting in fistfights and shoot-outs in our neighborhoods, in shopping malls, on the playground, and in school. It's disturbing and frightening, both for our nation's youth and for society as a whole.

If you've wanted to do something to stop this violence, then *Best Practices of Youth Violence Prevention: A Sourcebook for Community Action* is for you. We've pulled together the best practices known for four promising strategies to prevent youth violence, and we've organized them in a way that's easy to follow and use. And because it's often best to get expert advice "straight from the horse's mouth," we've included numerous resources to put you in touch with the people who have implemented these practices and seen the results.

Whether you're part of a grass-roots movement or involved with a large, established organization, you'll find this sourcebook to be a valuable asset to your youth violence prevention effort.

INTRODUCTION[1]

Violence among children and adolescents is a significant public health concern. In 1999,[1] violence claimed the lives of more than 3,200Americans ages 19 and under that's an average of 9 deaths per day—making the homicide rate for young people in the United States the highest among developed countries. Homicide is the second leading cause of death among 15- to 19-year-olds and the third leading cause of death among children ages 10 to 14.

Highly publicized school shootings have sobered communities that may have believed they were immune to youth violence. Once viewed as a problem only in inner-city neighborhoods, youth violence is now perceived as a nationwide crisis, and communities are eager to find ways to stop it.

Experts in youth violence prevention do not have all the answers for solving this public health problem; we must do a lot more research and evaluation. But we know enough to offer the public some insight into what works to prevent violence by children and adolescents. This book—which builds on CDC's 1993 publication *The Prevention of Youth Violence: A Framework for Community Action*—shares that insight.

We developed this book with input from individuals working to prevent youth violence and from individuals whose positions made them likely to play a role in violence prevention efforts. We interviewed teachers, school administrators, members of community-based organizations, employees and volunteers at social service agencies, health department personnel, program planners and practitioners, and researchers from universities across the

[1] Excerpted from Thornton TN, Craft CA, Dahlberg LL, Lynch BS, Baer K. *Best Practices of Youth Violence Prevention: A Sourcebook for Community Action (Rev.)*. Atlanta: Centers for Disease Control and Prevention, National Center for Injury Prevention and Control, 2002.

country to find out what they would like to see in a sourcebook for preventing violence by children and adolescents. Their responses guided the content and shaped the format of this book.

In addition to gathering information from experts, we conducted an extensive review of the scientific literature on youth violence prevention to collect the most up-to-date information available in the field. This literature review provides the science base on which our recommendations for best practices rest.

CONTENTS

This sourcebook places at your fingertips the best knowledge available about several strategies designed to prevent youth violence. These strategies are among those with the strongest evidence base for reducing youth violence.

Chapter 1 reviews general principals of intervention planning, implementation, and evaluation. This chapter will be especially helpful to readers who are new to developing prevention efforts. For seasoned program planners, it will be a useful refresher.

Chapter 2, the "meat" of the sourcebook, builds on the experiences of others who have worked to prevent violence by children and adolescents. It discusses in depth the best practices of four key youth prevention strategies and documents the science behind those best practices. Also in Chapter 2, you will find resources for more information about programs that have used these practices. We encourage you to talk with the organizations listed and to review the publications described to find out what worked particularly well and identify potential pitfalls and challenges.

The sourcebook also includes two appendices:

- Appendix A provides a fact sheet on the problem of youth violence. This information will be useful if you need to formulate a convincing appeal for support from organizations and community leaders.
- Appendix B provides an overview of the public health approach, the process by which public health problems are identified and addressed—and the underlying reason for our developing this sourcebook.

ENDNOTE

[1] The latest year for which data are available.

Chapter 1

PLANNING, IMPLEMENTING, AND EVALUATING AN INTERVENTION – AN OVERVIEW

INTRODUCTION

Planning, implementing, and evaluating an intervention can be a daunting project, especially for someone who has never been involved in such an effort. However, you can improve your chances of success if you follow certain steps. This chapter gives a brief overview of those steps.

In this chapter, we will explain how—and why—to do the following:

- Describe the problem of youth violence in your community
- Identify intended participants for an intervention
- Identify possible settings in which to reach intended participants
- Set goals and objectives
- Select an intervention interventions— address your goals and objectives and meet the needs of your participants
- Locate resources for your intervention
- Involve the community in your effort
- Develop activities and materials for your intervention
- Hire and train staff
- Monitor your intervention's progress
- Evaluate the success of your intervention

If after reading this chapter, you have questions or concerns about developing an intervention for your community, take a look at the *Additional Resources* section at the end of the chapter. The publications listed there contain helpful information about such topics as assessing a community's resources and readiness to change, working with diverse populations, and evaluating a program.

DEFINITIONS

You will see the terms strategy, intervention, and program repeated many times throughout this sourcebook. Because these terms may mean slightly different things to people in different professions, we have defined them here so all readers will know how they are used in this publication.

Strategy: A general conceptual approach to preventing violence by children and adolescents. For example, home visiting can offer basic training in parenting skills for pregnant teens.

Intervention: A specific set of activities and accompanying materials developed to prevent youth violence and the factors that contribute to it. For example, a school may implement a curriculum and role-playing activities to help students develop conflict-resolution skills.

Program: A grouping of strategies (and, therefore, of various kinds of interventions) designed to prevent youth violence. For example, a community might combine a school-based curriculum with a home-visiting intervention.

DESCRIBE THE PROBLEM

Before you can plan an intervention to prevent violence committed by children and adolescents in your community, you need an accurate description of the problem. This description will help you identify who is affected most by the problem and where the problem occurs most frequently so you can better target an intervention. It will guide you in developing realistic objectives for your intervention and will provide a baseline against which to measure progress. You also need a clear definition of the problem to convince lawmakers, community leaders, parents, volunteers, and potential funders that your intervention is necessary.

The information you need to describe the problem can be obtained from several sources. Quantitative data is available from a number of agencies and organizations that collect statistics on youth violence, and you can interview or survey members of your community to get qualitative information (e.g., opinions, attitudes). Regardless of where you get your information, be sure the individuals collecting it are respected and trusted by the community.

Factual Information

Many sources of data exist to help you define the problem of youth violence in your community. Table 1 lists some of those sources. Appendix A at the end of this sourcebook also provides data about youth violence at a national level. Before asking agencies and organizations for information, do a little research.

> *Before you plan an intervention to prevent violence committed by children and adolescents in your community, you need an accurate description of the problem.*

Table 1 Sources of Factual Information about Youth Violence

Police records
Vital statistics division of state or local health department
Medical examiner
Hospital or emergency department records
Outpatient records from public or private clinics
Emergency medical service (ambulance) records
School s records, attendance records, and records of disciplinary infractions
Youth risk behavior surveys (see *Additional Resources* for details)
Federal agencies (see *Additional Resources* for details)

Find out what information each entity has and limit your request to that information. Don't send out one blanket request to several agencies, hoping to find information you need.

Because information about children and adolescents who commit violent acts is often kept confidential, you may have to get summary data. Summary data provide the statistics without any information that could identify the people involved. If you are working with a research organization or university, its staff should know how to get legal access to records.

Once you know how many young people committed violent acts, when and where the acts took place, and what circumstances surrounded those acts, you may want to find out about factors in your community that could contribute to violence. Examples of contributing factors include racism, poverty, unemployment, and other social, cultural, or economic conditions. Some of this information can be obtained from the U.S. Census (available through your local library), the Department of Labor's employment statistics, and the Department of Housing and Urban Development.

Opinions from Community Members

How do members of your community perceive the problem of youth violence, and what do they think is causing it? To find out, survey residents, community leaders, school personnel, legal and police personnel, health workers, and parents. For example, ask school principals and guidance counselors about violence they see in the schools and listen to their ideas for reducing it. Talk to young people, particularly those who might be in trouble or at risk for trouble (for example, those who are expelled from school). Contact the youths and their parents at home and in as many community sites as possible, including supermarkets, shopping centers, basketball courts and other recreational areas, churches, and schools. Local colleges and universities may be able to help with opinion surveys.

Opinion surveys and interviews are valuable because they help you collect information that does not appear in the statistics. The survey responses help assess community members' beliefs, knowledge, and attitudes about youth violence. They may also identify social norms and determine community priorities. And you may learn about ideas for possible interventions.

Data Interpretation

The data you obtain from statistical reports and opinion surveys may need to be analyzed and interpreted before you can use it. Enlist a statistician or other expert to help make your data easy to understand before you present it to community leaders. After you have the data about your community, compare it with that of your state and the U.S. overall. This comparison will provide community leaders with some perspective.

> *Once you know how many young people committed violent acts, when and where the acts took place, and what circumstances surrounded those acts, you may want to find out about factors in your community that could contribute to violence.*

SELECT INTENDED PARTICIPANT GROUPS

An intended participant group is the group of people your intervention is designed to influence. The data you collected about your community will guide your decision about whom to target. This group may be general or specific, depending on the youth violence problem in your community and the resources available to address it. Table 2 lists potential participant groups.

General Population of Children and Adolescents

Interventions directed at all children in a community typically require a lot of resources and, therefore, can be very expensive. The benefit of these broad interventions is that you reach a large number of young people with violence-prevention messages. The down side is that they may not affect high-risk youth as much as targeted interventions.

At-Risk and High-Risk Children and Adolescents

Research has shown that certain factors make children and adolescents more susceptible to developing violent behavior. These factors include an individual's characteristics or behaviors, including a history of aggression; beliefs that support the use of violence; social or cognitive problems; and the use of alcohol or drugs. They also include family and community circumstances such as a parent's use of alcohol or drugs; a lack of parental supervision or discipline; spousal abuse or child abuse; poor emotional attachment between parent and child; access to firearms; and divorce, relocation, or other family disruption. Problems at school, such as chronic discipline problems and associating with peers who are violent, can also put a young person at risk for developing violent behavior (Dahlberg 1998).

**Table 2 Potential Participant Groups for Interventions
to Prevent Youth Violence**

All children and adolescents in a community
All children in a specific age group, school, grade
Children and adolescents with risk factors such as
       use of alcohol or other drugs
       history of early aggression
       social or learning problems
       exposure to violence at home, in their neighborhood, or in the
          media
       parental drug or alcohol use
       friends who engage in problem behavior
       academic failure or poor commitment to school
       poverty
       recent divorce, relocation, or other family disruption
       access to firearms
Children and adolescents with high-risk behaviors such as
       criminal activity
       fighting or victimization
       drug or alcohol abuse
       selling drugs
       carrying a weapon
       membership in a gang
       dropping out of school
       unemployment
       homelessness
       recent immigration
Parents and other family members
Influential adults such as
       teachers
       coaches
       child care providers
General population of a community

High-risk individuals are those who consistently engage in physical fights to resolve problems, have a criminal record, have a history of inflicting violent injury, have been the victim of violence, have failed or dropped out of school, carry a weapon, belong to a gang, or use drugs. Children and adolescents who move a lot, including children of immigrants or migrant workers, are also considered high risk.

If you choose to target at-risk or high-risk groups, be prepared for special challenges. You may need to enlist outreach workers to locate and engage high-risk youths, many of whom are no longer in school. You may also find it hard to establish trust and receptiveness among these young people.

Young Children (10 Years and Younger)

Violence is a learned behavior. The values, attitudes, and interpersonal skills acquired early in life play a key role in the development of violent behavior. Because a person's violent or nonviolent tendencies may be set in early childhood, preschool-and elementary school-age children are often thought to be ideal participants in interventions that promote nonviolent values and enhance conflict-resolution skills.

Parents and Other Family Members

Family experiences play a critical role in causing, promoting, or reinforcing violent behavior by children and adolescents. Therefore, it is important to develop interventions targeted to parents, siblings, or the entire family unit. Interventions that involve the family often complement interventions carried out in the schools or other parts of the community.

Other Influential Adults

Parents are not the only adults who shape the beliefs and behavior of young people. Individuals such as teachers, coaches, child care providers, and neighbors often influence how a child or adolescent feels about violence. As with interventions targeting family members, interventions that involve other adults in the community may be effective in supporting the interventions that target the young people themselves.

General Population

Social norms affect how violence is portrayed, whether violence by young people is tolerated, and how many resources a community will devote to stopping youth violence. Interventions for the general population can increase knowledge about the magnitude of youth violence in a community, help inform legislation or policies regarding youth violence, and create an environment that fosters and supports other interventions to prevent violence by young people. However, as with interventions targeting all young people in a community, efforts designed to change the values, attitudes, or behaviors of the entire community are costly. And they may fail to reach those most in need of change.

> *The values, attitudes, and interpersonal skills acquired early in life play a key role in the development of violent behavior.*

SELECT A SETTING

The setting for an intervention is where activities will occur. Select a setting that is convenient and comfortable for participants; ask them where they would like to meet. Also consider the type of intervention you are planning. While many interventions have a logical setting, others—especially those targeting high-risk youth—may be less obvious. You may need to collect additional data about your intended participants to determine where your intervention can be carried out most effectively. Table 3 lists possible settings for interventions to prevent youth violence.

SET GOALS AND OBJECTIVES

Once you have identified whom you should reach with an intervention and where to reach them,[2] decide what the goal of your intervention will be. Your goal should be a broad statement of what you want to achieve. Then determine the specific things you will need to do to achieve your goal. These are your objectives. Objectives should be measurable and attainable given the resources you have. They should tell who should achieve how much of what, where it should occur, and by when (NCIPC 1993). Table 4 provides an example of a goal and its corresponding objectives.

Table 3 Possible Settings for Interventions to Prevent Youth Violence

General population of young people
    schools
    churches
    playgrounds
    youth activity centers
    homes
    shopping centers and malls
    movie theaters
High-risk youth
    alternative schools
    juvenile justice facilities
    social service facilities
    mental health and medical care facilities
    hospital emergency departments
    recreation centers
Young children
    child care centers
    homes
    schools
Parents
    homes
    workplaces
    churches
    community centers

Objectives are important because they clarify the tasks to be done and provide a means of tracking an intervention's progress. If you have many objectives, consider grouping them by the type of outcome— health effects such as injuries or deaths; behaviors such as fighting, expulsions, or dropping out of school; or other aspects of the program such as the number of students in a class or the number of newspaper articles published about youth violence. Presenting the objectives this way may make it easier for community leaders, supporters, funders, and others to see what you are trying to achieve.

Keep these important guidelines in mind when developing your goal and objectives:

- Make sure they fit the characteristics and resources of your community.
- If you are working with other organizations, get their input to ensure that the goals and objectives of the intervention are consistent with those of each organization.
- Do not include objectives to satisfy another organization's research agenda if they are unrelated to your goal. (However, it may be worthwhile to make minor additions to your objectives if doing so will generate substantial resources for your effort.)

Remember, your objectives are not static. Modify them as new information becomes available, as resources change, or as activities proceed faster or more slowly than planned.

Table 4 Example of a Goal and Its Objectives Goal: Reduce expulsions resulting from fights in middle schools.

Objectives:

1. By 2000, offer a 25-lesson program in 6th-grade classes to help students develop social skills and learn non-aggressive responses appropriate for dealing with conflict.
    Who: Prevention specialists
    What: 1-hour sessions offered twice a week for one school year on topics such as self-understanding, conflict resolution, anger control, and pro-social actions
    How much: All 6th-grade classes
    When: By 2000
    Where: Columbia County schools
 	
2. By 2001, implement a school-wide program to mediate behavior problems and disputes between adolescents. *Who:* Teachers and peer mediators
    What: Weekly mediation clinics
    How much: All 6th-, 7th-, and 8th-grade students
    When: By 2001
    Where: Columbia County schools

Table 4 Continued

3. By 2002, reduce the number of fights among 8th-grade students from five per month to two per month.

  Who: Middle school students
  What: Incidents of physical aggression
  How much: Reduce by 60 percent
  When: By 2002
  Where: Columbia County schools

4. By 2004, reduce by half the number of middle school students (grades 6 through 8) expelled because of fights or other disruptive incidents in the schools.

  Who: Middle school students
  What: Expulsions related to fights in schools
  How much: Reduce from an average of two per
  month to one per month
  When: By 2004
  Where: Columbia County schools

Objectives clarify the tasks to be done and provide a means of tracking an intervervention's progress.

SELECT AN APPROPRIATE INTERVENTION

We can teach young people how to avoid violent situations. We can help them develop the skills they need to resolve conflicts without resorting to violence. We can help parents provide a nonviolent home for their children. We can provide young people with mentors who serve as nonviolent role models.

With so many types of interventions, how do you choose? Start by reviewing the characteristics of your community and your intended participants. Also consider the most appropriate settings for your intervention, based on research about the intended participants. And review your goals and objectives. The intervention you choose should best suit all of these factors. It should also be appropriate given your resources.

Build on the experience of others. If you know of interventions that have worked in other communities similar to yours, use them as models for your effort. Chapter 2 of this sourcebook offers many examples of interventions and the best practices for planning and implementing them. Keep in mind, however, that you may need to modify an intervention to make it appropriate to your community.

Selecting Multiple Interventions

A single intervention conducted in isolation is not likely to solve the problem of youth violence; too many factors contribute to violent behavior to be addressed by one strategy. The most effective programs include several types of interventions and strategies that complement one another. For example, a mentoring program to help teens avoid gang membership may be complemented by an intervention that offers alternative after-school activities. Instruction on nonviolent conflict resolution for school children may be complemented by an intervention that teaches families how to foster nonviolence at home. Carefully consider your resources, community support, and level of experience when selecting interventions. And make sure that the interventions you choose fit together well.

LOCATE RESOURCES FOR YOUR INTERVENTION

Implementing an intervention to prevent violence by young people takes a variety of resources. Funding and other material resources—such as office space, equipment, and supplies critical to your effort. But they, alone, do not ensure success. You also need a commitment of time, effort, and support from the members of your community. These resources may come from public or private sources. You can also generate your own resources by organizing fundraisers and other events that publicize your effort.

> *Build on the experience of others. If you know of interventions that have worked in other communities similar to yours, use them as models for your effort.*

Public Sources

Public funds come from federal, state, and local governments. Government agencies typically retain a great deal of control over how the money is spent because they are held accountable to the public. However, these agencies often provide substantial funding and may be easier to locate than private entities.

It may be easiest to start with local and state government agencies. If they don't have funds available, they can refer you to other government sources. Contact your local health department, department of housing, human resources or social services agency, department of parks and recreation, and department of education or school board. While few states publish a directory of available funds, many have web sites that tell you whom to contact about potential funding. You might also identify funding sources through personal contacts, such as elected officials. The Public Health Foundation is also a valuable source for funding information. They compile information on program areas that are funded in each state. You can reach the Foundation at www.phf.org or 202-898-5600.

When contacting state and local officials, ask about block grants. Each state receives federal block grants to support activities in four key public health areas: preventive health; maternal and child health; alcohol, drug abuse, and mental health; and primary care. Table 5 provides contacts for information about block grants.

Federal agencies offer other funding in addition to block grants. There are several ways to find these resources. Agencies solicit proposals and grant applications in the *Federal Register* and the *Commerce Business Daily*. You can subscribe to these publications through the Government Printing Office by calling 202-512-1800 or visiting their web site at www.access.gpo.gov/su_docs. However, these subscriptions are expensive. You may find it more practical to review these publications in your local library or to access them on the Internet. Research using these two publications will be time-consuming, regardless of how you access them.

The *Catalog of Federal Domestic Assistance* is another source of information about federal funding. Published annually, the catalog describes major federal grants and contracts, outlines eligibility requirements, identifies criteria for selection, explains financial details, and provides contact information. Because the information in this publication can become outdated quickly, you should contact each agency before submitting a proposal. The *Catalog of Federal Domestic Assistance* is available from the Government Printing Office: 202-512-1800 or www.access.gpo.gov/su_docs.

Table 5 Contacts for Information about Block Grants

Preventive Health
Centers for Disease Control and Prevention
Procurement and Grants Office
2920 Brandywine Road
Suite 3000, Mailstop E-13
Atlanta, GA 30341-4146
770-488-2800
www.cdc.gov/od/pgo/funding/grantmain.htm

Maternal and Child Health
Health Resources and Services Administration
Division of Maternal and Child Health
Parklawn Building, Room 18-05
5600 Fishers Lane
Rockville, MD 20857
301-443-0205
www.mchb.hrsa.gov/html/grantsguidance.html

Alcohol, Drug Abuse, and Mental Health
Substance Abuse and Mental Health Services Administration
Division of Grants and Contract Management
Parklawn Building, Room 15C-05
5600 Fishers Lane
Rockville, MD 20857
301-443-4456
www.samhsa.gov/GRANT/GFA_KDA.HTM

Primary Care
Health Resources and Services Administration
Division of Primary Care Services
8th Floor, East West Towers Building
4350 East West Highway
Bethesda, MD 20814
301-594-4100
www.bphc.hrsa.dhhs.gov

The *Additional Resources* section of this chapter can also help you locate potential public funding sources. It contains a list of federal agencies with an interest in youth violence prevention, some of which provide grant money. You will need to contact them directly to find out if your intervention is of interest to them and if you meet their criteria.

Private Sources

Private funds come from corporations and other businesses, voluntary organizations, foundations, charitable institutions, churches, and other local establishments. Private organizations are typically more flexible than public agencies in the types of interventions they fund, and they often have less direct involvement in and oversight of the intervention. These organizations may also offer facilities, equipment, and volunteers.

While the process for requesting support tends to be less formal with private entities, you still need to convince their decision makers that your intervention is worthy of their resources. Provide them with data you gathered about youth violence in your community and explain how your intervention will address the problem. Share your goals and objectives. You may also need to show the business or organization how their involvement will benefit them directly (for example, increased visibility if you list them as a sponsor).

Corporations and Businesses

Ask local businesses—your program. They can often provide funds or give you office space, equipment, and other supplies needed for your intervention. U.S. corporations donate a great deal of money each year to help communities address public health issues. Look for a large company with facilities in your area and ask for their financial support.

Voluntary, Community Service, and Religious Organizations

Community groups or local divisions of state or national voluntary organizations (such as the Child Welfare League of America, Children's Safety Network, National Crime Prevention Council, and KidsPeace) may be willing to donate funds or other materials to your effort. Community service groups such as sororities, fraternities, and associations of retired teachers will often provide volunteers to carry out your intervention. Churches and religious organizations may offer resources such as meeting space for intervention activities.

Hospitals and Other Health Care Facilities

These facilities may have meeting space you can use for intervention activities. Mental health services staff and pediatricians may help you enroll participants by referring patients to your program.

Local Television and Radio Stations and Newspapers

Community media may be willing to provide free publicity for your program, through announcements, interviews, and human interest stories. Local media personalities may also take part in fundraising efforts and other activities.

Educational Institutions

Schools, including local colleges and universities, may be able to provide volunteers for your intervention and help conduct fundraisers. Universities may be willing to help you conduct research and develop your intervention.

Foundations

A foundation's sole purpose is philanthropic giving. Many foundations are willing to fund programs with good ideas but little experience. They are more likely than public agencies to take a chance on a new intervention. Because foundations may limit the types of interventions they fund or the geographic areas they serve, it is important to find out which foundations support violence prevention interventions. The Foundation Center can help you do that.

The Foundation Center provides detailed information about the interests and restrictions of individual foundations and about the money they have granted. They have four main offices as well as libraries in all 50 states. To locate the nearest Foundation Center library, call 800-424-9836 or visit www.fdncenter.org. You can also find listings of foundations and their areas of interest in your public library.

After identifying a foundation as a potential funding source, write a letter to the foundation that briefly states what you want to do in the community and ask whether the foundation is interested in this type of project. Through this inquiry, you will also find out the process for submitting a grant proposal.

INVOLVE THE COMMUNITY

Involving the community in planning your intervention will benefit you, the intended participants, and the community as a whole. When community members are asked to help plan and implement the intervention, they develop a sense of ownership. They want the intervention to succeed and are more willing to invest the effort and resources needed to sustain it. Involving the community also makes it easier to obtain the resources and volunteers you need to carry out your intervention.

Table 6 Organizations that May Collaborate in Youth Violence Prevention Efforts

Government and Community Agencies and Organizations
Health department
Social services agencies
Mental health agencies
Department of Education
Police department
Judicial system
Fire department
Housing authority
Schools, including alternative
    schools
Agricultural extension service
Tribal councils
Neighborhood associations
Tenant councils

Volunteer Service Organizations
Service fraternities/sororities
National Network of Runaway and
    Youth Services
Veterans organizations
Salvation Army
Goodwill Industries

Clubs
Big Brothers/Big Sisters
Boys and Girls Clubs
Girl Scouts/Boy Scouts
Other youth clubs

Professional Groups
Medical associations
Nursing associations
Schools of public health
Associations of psychologists (APA)
Associations of sociologists (ASA)
Associations of anthropologists
Legal associations (American Bar Assn)
Social workers associations
Teachers associations (PTA, NEA)

Private Organizations (for profit and nonprofit)
Foundations
NAACP
Urban League
Churches/religious organizations
General and specialty hospitals,
    including mental health hospitals
Colleges and universities
Local businesses
Media outlets, including newspaper,
    radio, and television
YMCA/YWCA
Entertainers
Professional sports organizations
Domestic violence prevention groups
Center for the Improvement of Child
    Caring

So what's the best way to involve the community? From the very beginning, enlist organizations and agencies that know about the youth in your community and have an interest in preventing injury and death among young people. Institutions that frequently get involved in efforts to prevent youth violence include schools, churches, parks and recreation centers, businesses, and civic, service, and cultural groups.

The Foundation Center:
800-424-9836 www.fdncenter.org

Table 6 provides other ideas of community organizations that may offer important input and be interested in collaborating to prevent youth violence. Not every group listed in the table is appropriate for every community. And this list is not exhaustive—consider all organizations in your community. To increase collaboration, you may want to establish a youth violence prevention committee in your community.

In addition to involving organizations, get input and support from influential individuals. High-ranking officials, such as the town mayor or a state representative, can help you gain support for your intervention. Be sure to involve parents. Their support—or the lack of it—can greatly affect the success of your intervention.

Coordinating Efforts

Once you have commitments from organizations that want to help you develop and implement your intervention, you need to decide what they are going to do and how to keep them working in harmony. Establish a leadership structure that includes members of the community and intended participant groups. Leadership roles may be informal and flexible until your intervention takes shape. However, as activities develop, leaders will be more formally designated, and their responsibilities—as well as those of the others involved in the effort—will clearly be delineated. Documenting the division of duties before an intervention is launched will help prevent duplication of effort and potential "turf wars" between organizations. It will also help you identify organizations that need technical assistance in order to prepare for and carry out their assigned activities.

DEVELOP YOUR ACTIVITIES AND MATERIALS

At this point, you have planned many of the key elements of your intervention—where you can reach them, what your goals and objectives are, and whom you will work with to achieve them. Now, it's time to develop the activities and materials that your intervention will comprise.

Involving representatives of your intended participant group in this process is crucial. Conduct focus groups and surveys to identify participant's needs, potential barriers, and cultural issues. This input will help you tailor your intervention to meet the needs and preferences of participants.

Considering Culture

Cultural diversity is a term used to describe the differences found in our society due to race, ethnicity, religious beliefs, economic status, sexual orientation, and many other factors. These differences affect directly observable behavioral characteristics of a group such as language and dialect, verbal and nonverbal communication styles, customs, religious observances, dance, music, and child-rearing practices. They also affect characteristics that are less obvious, such as attitudes, values, and the ways in which we interpret the behaviors and actions of others (Szalay 1978).

Most research indicates that cultural factors, such as race, have little to do with an individual's tendency to be violent. However, these factors have a lot to do with how people respond to an intervention. Therefore, when developing the activities and materials for your intervention, you must consider the cultural characteristics of your intended participants. These characteristics will help shape the tone, content, source, and style of your activities and messages.

Pretesting Materials and Activities

Before you launch your intervention, test the activities and materials with representatives of your intended participant group. Pretesting will allow you to see whether your materials and activities achieve the desired outcome. It will also reveal any undesired effects. It will help you verify whether messages are accepted and understood by participants and whether the reading level of written materials is appropriate.

STAFF YOUR INTERVENTION

Once your intervention is developed, you need a staff to implement it. The composition of your staff will depend on several factors. First, think about the activities to be conducted. Some interventions will require a staff with specialized skills or formal education. For example, you may need registered nurses or licensed social workers to perform home visits. You must also consider the needs and preferences of your intended participants. If, for example, you learn that young boys prefer male mentors of the same race and ethnicity, staff your intervention accordingly.

Another big consideration is the resources available for your effort. If your intervention is well-funded, you may be able to hire several paid staff members. On the other hand, if you have limited resources (which is often the case) you will need to enlist volunteers. You may have already identified volunteers when you secured funding and other resources.

Also think about how much time your staff will need to spend working on your intervention. An intervention that involves home visits may require full-time staff members who can visit several homes each day. In contrast, an intervention that involves parenting classes at a community center may need only part-time staffers to teach classes a few evenings a week. In many cases, you may need individuals who can implement your intervention in conjunction with their other job duties. For example, you may ask coaches at the YMCA to implement a violence prevention curriculum during team practices.

TRAIN YOUR STAFF

Whatever the content of your intervention or the staff you select, everyone involved in implementing the intervention the administrative staff and others working behind the scenes must receive training. This training should inform staff members about the problem of youth violence in your community and teach them how to carry out your intervention's activities. Even professionals who have completed formal education or who have worked on violence prevention efforts before will benefit from training specific to your intervention.

> *Everyone involved in implementing the intervention must receive training.*

Training Content and Schedule

Training content will depend, of course, on your intervention activities and materials, but the following elements are applicable to all staff members and all interventions.

- **Communication skills.** How your staff communicates—both verbally and nonverbally—can affect the success of your intervention. Train your staff to communicate in a way that expresses respect for participant's situations; staff members must never be condescending or judgmental. They must convey confidence in participant's ability to perform the intervention's activities. And they must model the types of behavior encouraged in the intervention. Teach skills such as active listening, nonviolent responses to conflict, and positive reinforcement.

- **Team building.** It is extremely important to provide training experiences that enhance camaraderie among all staff members—both paid and volunteer. Volunteers must be treated as invaluable members of your staff, and they must receive acceptance and support from paid personnel. The absence of this acceptance and support is a primary reason for attrition of volunteers. Including team-building exercises can improve the cohesiveness of your staff and improve performance.

- **Intervention content.** All staff members should be familiar with the scope of youth violence in your community and should understand how your intervention can prevent that violence. Provide a comprehensive overview of your intervention's activities, the objects of those activities, and how to overcome possible barriers to achieving those objectives. It may be helpful to explain the public health approach, the process by which public health problems—such as youth violence— are identified and addressed. (See Appendix B for an overview of the public health approach.)

- **Training manual.** Develop a manual that staffers can refer to after they finish training. Include a summary or outline of the information discussed in the training, as well as exercises designed to help trainees practice the skills they have learned. Also include the intervention's procedures and operations, forms required for record keeping and data collection, and names and phone numbers of persons to contact with questions or concerns about implementing the intervention.

- **Skills practice.** Include time for trainees to practice new skills by role playing segments of your intervention. Offer feedback about their performance and encourage other trainees to do so. Give staff members an opportunity to evaluate their own performance, too.
- **Ongoing training.** Plan for additional training sessions during implementation of your intervention. These sessions can address difficulties that arise during implementation and provide additional skill-building activities to enhance your staff's performance. They can also help keep momentum going among staff members.

While there is no single formula for training, one day of training in a large group is clearly inadequate. Ideally, intervention-specific training should be conducted by personnel from or endorsed by the organization that developed and evaluated the intervention. However, when this is not feasible, provide materials that in-house staff can use to conduct the training. It is also helpful to offer a "train-the-trainer" curriculum so in-house trainers can better prepare.

Whatever the format used, training should be conducted at a time that is convenient for your staff. If you have a full-time, paid staff, all-day sessions during the week are appropriate. However, if your staff consists mainly of part-time employees or volunteers who have other jobs, conduct weekend or evening sessions that do not interfere with those other commitments. Or ask employers to pay their employees for the time spent in training—ay of supporting their community.

Before Training Begins

Before you conduct training, assess each staff member's readiness to learn violence prevention skills and implement the activities that compose your intervention. You can do this by measuring the extent to which individuals agree with three statements (Slaby 1998):

- People's violent behavior can be prevented (general beliefs).
- Particular interventions can be effective in helping to prevent violence (specific beliefs).
- I, myself, can make a difference in helping to prevent violence (personal beliefs).

If you find that members of your staff do not agree with these statements, you will need to start your training session with activities to help individuals overcome their doubts. Providing evidence of successful interventions may help convince your staff that its efforts can, in fact, impact youth violence.

Implement Your Intervention

You've developed your materials and activities. You've secured resources and personnel. You've trained your staff. Now it's time to implement your intervention.

Implementation will vary greatly from intervention to intervention in terms of duration (how long the intervention lasts), frequency (how many times in a given period activities occur), and intensity (how much material is covered and how much time is spent during each activity). Chapter 2 addresses these issues for each of four strategies for preventing youth violence. With all interventions, however, you will need to supervise and support your staff, maintain a consistent level of participation, and keep the community interested in your intervention. Chapter 2 offers guidance on these matters, as well.

Monitor Your Intervention

During all phases of your intervention, monitoring the implementation process is essential. Intervention monitoring will let you see if activities are occurring according to your plan. It will also allow you to identify unanticipated problems or barriers.

> *With all interventions, you will need to supervise and support your staff, maintain a consistent level of participation, and keep the community interested in your intervention.*

Methods for monitoring interventions will vary (Chapter 2 addresses some issues specific to the four strategies), but at a minimum, intervention monitoring should include the following:

- **Measurement of key variables to see if your objectives are being met.** For example, if one of your objectives is to implement a school-wide program to improve students'conflict-resolution skills, you might measure how many times in a semester skill-building activities were conducted. You might also measure student attendance during the activities.
- **Evaluations by intervention staff.** This information can tell you whether staff members feel their training prepared them adequately for conducting a particular activity, whether participants seem comfortable with staff members and with the activity, and whether instructions for the activity were clear to participants.
- **Feedback from participants about the intervention's activities.** For example, you might assess whether participants enjoyed a particular activity and how well they understood the materials presented. You might also ask whether participants would change anything about the activity.

Review the data regularly. If you find that an activity is not achieving the outcome you desired, you may need to alter it. If staffers report that they are having a hard time implementing an activity, you may need to provide additional training. If you discover that activities are not being implemented as often as planned or that participation is much lower than anticipated, you may need to reexamine your objectives; perhaps they were overly ambitious for your intervention's time frame or resources. Whatever changes you make—whether to activities, materials, or objectives—be sure to inform all intervention staff members and supporters.

EVALUATE YOUR INTERVENTION

Throughout your intervention you will monitor progress to make sure you are on track and on schedule. At the end of your intervention, you must do a final (or summative) evaluation to determine how well you achieved your goals and objectives. You'll assess how well you reached your intended participants and whether the outcomes you obtained were what you planned. You'll also compare the costs of the program with the benefits of the program. You may also plan a follow-up study to assess the long-term effects of your efforts.

Many organizations have limited resources and may be tempted to skip evaluation, instead dedicating that money to intervention activities.

However, evaluation is a critical step. It will enable you to demonstrate to funders, community leaders, and intervention staff that your efforts were a success. And if your intervention fell short of expectations, evaluation will help you identify what went wrong so you can make necessary changes to the intervention (Thompson and McClintock 1998).

If your organization does not have the expertise needed to evaluate your intervention but has resources to devote to it, you can hire a consultant. If you lack resources for evaluation, partner with a local university that would be willing to design and carry out a scientific evaluation.

Evaluation is a critical step. It will enable you to demonstrate to funders, community leaders, and intervention staff that your efforts were a success.

SUMMARY

The steps involved in intervention planning, implementation, and evaluation may seem time-consuming, labor-intensive, even overwhelming. However, by following this systematic process, you will increase the likelihood of your intervention's success and enable others to repeat your intervention in their communities.

REFERENCES

Dahlberg LL. "Youth Violence in the United States: Major Trends, Risk Factors, and Prevention Approaches. *American Journal of Preventive Medicine* 1998;14(4):259-272.

National Center for Injury Prevention and Control. *The Prevention of Youth Violence: A Framework for Community Action.* Atlanta: Centers for Disease Control and Prevention, 1993.

Slaby RG. "Preventing Youth Violence Through Research-Guided Intervention." In Trickett PK, Schellenbach C, editors. *Violence Against Children in the Family and the Community.* Washington, DC: American Psychological Association, 1998: 371-399.

Szalay LB. *The Hispanic Cultural Frame of Reference: A Communication Guide for Use in Mental Health, Education, and Training.* Washington, DC: Institute for Comparative Social and Cultural Studies, 1978.

Thompson NJ, McClintock HO. *Demonstrating Your Program's Worth: A Primer on Evaluation for Programs to Prevent Unintentional Injury.* Atlanta: Centers for Disease Control and Prevention, National Center for Injury Prevention and Control, 1998.

ADDITIONAL RESOURCES

Publications

The following publications provide information about youth violence in America and about planning, implementing, and evaluating interventions to prevent it.

Baucher E, Lamison-White L. *Poverty in the United States,* 1995. U.S. Bureau of the Census, Current Population Reports, Series P60-194. Washington, DC: U.S. Government Printing Office, 1996. Provides statistics on children who live in poverty.

Elliott DS, Hamburg BA, Williams KR. *Violence in American Schools: A New Perspective.* New York: Cambridge University Press, 1998. (www.cup.org) This anthology presents an overview of the problem of violence in American schools. It discusses an integrated approach to violence prevention that includes school- and community-based interventions.

Fox JA. *Trends in Juvenile Violence: 1997 Update.* Washington, DC: Bureau of Justice Statistics, U.S. Department of Justice, 1997. (www.ojp.usdoj.gov/bjs/abstract/tjvfox.htm) This report discusses demographic trends and their impact on crime. It concludes that the growth in juvenile population in the next decade will cause a dramatic increase in the level of juvenile violence. This report, produced under a Bureau of Justice Statistics grant, updates Dr. Fox's briefing of the Attorney General in 1995.

Gonzalez VM, Gonzalez JT, Freeman V. *Health Promotion in Diverse Cultural Communities.* Palo Alto, CA: Health Promotion Resource Center, Stanford Center for Research in Disease Prevention, 1991. (http://scrdp.stanford.edu) This book presents practical guidelines for working in and with culturally diverse communities. The guidelines are written in such a way as to avoid perpetuating cultural stereotypes. They suggest ways to learn about the cultural characteristics of a community, with the understanding that each community's cultural identity and background is diverse and dynamic.

Goodman RM, Speers MA, McLeroy K, Fawcett S, Kegler M, Parker E, et al. "Identifying and Defining the Dimensions of Community Capacity to Provide a Basis for Measurement." *Health Education and Behavior* **1998;25(3):258-278.** This article describes the dimensions that are central to community capacity, including participation and leadership, skills, resources, social and inter-organizational networks, sense of community, understanding of community history, community power, community values, and critical reflection.

Haglund B, Weisbrod RR, Bracht N. "Assessing the Community: Its Services, Needs, Leadership, and Readiness.". *Health Promotion at the Community Level.* **Newbury Park, CA: Sage Publications, Inc., 1990: 91-108.** This chapter discusses the importance of community analysis, the process of assessing and defining needs, opportunities, and resources of a community. It identifies methods for collecting both quantitative and qualitative data, including suggestions for special studies to increase information about selected social groups in a community. Community analysis is a critical first step in shaping the design of an intervention and in tailoring the implementation plan to a community's characteristics.

Heaney CA, Israel BA. "Social Networks and Social Support." *Health Behavior and Health Education*, **2nd ed. San Francisco: Jossey-Bass Inc., 1997: 179-205.** This chapter provides a conceptual overview of the link between social relationships and health. It briefly reviews the empirical support for that link, discusses intervention implications, and presents two cases illustrating how the health-enhancing potential of social relationships has been incorporated into health education practice.

Kaufman P, Chen X, Choy SP, Ruddy S, Miller A, Chandler K, et al. *Indicators of School Crime and Safety, 1999.* **Washington, DC: U.S. Departments of Education and Justice, 1999. NCES 1999-057/NCJ-178906. (www.ojp.usdoj.gov/bjs/abstract/iscs99.htm)** This is the second edition of *Indicators of School Crime and Safety,* a joint effort by the Bureau of Justice Statistics and the National Center for Education Statistics. The report, which provides detailed statistical information about the current nature of crime in schools, is a companion document to the *Annual Report on School Safety: 1999*. The annual report, a joint publication of the Departments of Education and Justice, provides an overview of the nature and scope of school crime and describes actions schools and communities can take to address this critical issue. The two reports respond to a 1998 request by President Clinton for an annual report card on school violence.

Linney JA, Wandersman A. *Prevention Plus III: Assessing Alcohol and Other Drug Prevention Programs at the School and Community Level.* **Rockville, MD: Office for Substance Abuse Prevention, 1991. DHHS [pub. no. (ADM) 91-1817].** **(www.health.org/pubs/catalog/ index.htm)** This workbook was developed to help programs with limited resources and expertise assess their programs in order to make informed decisions about resource allocation and program enhancement.

Milstein RL, Wetterhall SF, CDC Evaluation Working Group. "Framework for Program Evaluation in Public Health." *MMWR Recommendations and Reports,* **September 17, 1999.** *MMWR* **1999;48 (RR11):1-40.** This report summarizes the essential elements of program evaluation and encourages their integration with routine program operations. The emphasis is on practical, ongoing evaluation strategies that involve all stakeholders, not just evaluation experts.

Pirie PL. "Evaluating Health Promotion Programs: Basic Questions and Approaches." In: Bracht N, editor. *Health Promotion at the Community Level.* **Newbury Park, CA: Sage Publications, Inc., 1990: 201-208.** This chapter addresses the concerns of individuals who are under pressure to evaluate their programs but consider evaluation to be a low priority in view of other program needs. It provides a framework for demonstrating the value of evaluation to program planners, participants, and supporters.

Silberman M, Auerbach C. *Active Training: A Handbook of Techniques, Designs, Case Examples, and Tips.* **New York: Lexington Books, 1990.** A complete guide on designing and conducting a training program, this book addresses how to assess the training group, develop training objectives, create alternative methods to lecturing, sequence training activities, and prepare oneself as trainer.

Snyder HN, Sickmund M. *Juvenile Offenders and Victims: 1999 National Report.* **Washington, DC: Office of Juvenile Justice and Delinquency Prevention, U.S. Department of Justice, September 1999. (www.ncjrs.org/html/ojjdp/nationalreport99/toc.html)** This report consolidates, in a user-friendly format, the most requested statistics on juvenile offenders and victims. National data were used when available. The document also lists other government sources that provide information on the topics covered in the report.

Thompson NJ, McClintock HO. *Demonstrating Your Program's Worth: A Primer on Evaluation for Programs to Prevent Unintentional Injury.* **Atlanta: Centers for Disease Control and Prevention, National Center for Injury Prevention and Control, 1998. (www.cdc.gov/ncipc/pubres/demonstr.htm)** This book discusses why program evaluation is important and provides guidance on conducting simple evaluation, hiring and supervising consultants for complex evaluation, and incorporating evaluation activities into a program's activities. Although it is focused on unintentional injuries, the principles apply to violence-related injuries, as well.

U.S. Department of Commerce. *Marital Status and Living Arrangements.* **U.S. Bureau of the Census, Current Population Survey. Washington, DC: U.S. Government Printing Office 1996. Publication no. PPL-52.** Provides data on children who live with parents or others and the amount of parental supervision they receive.

U.S. Department of Health and Human Services. *Making Health Communication Programs Work—A Planner's Guide.* **Bethesda, MD: National Institutes of Health, 1992. NIH Publication No. 92-1493. (http://rex.nci.nih.gov/NCI_Pub_Interface/   HCPW/HOME.HTM)** Although this publication is geared toward developing communication programs, the principles can be applied to planning, implementing, and evaluating any intervention.
Available online only.

Federal Data Sources

The following federal government agencies have useful data about youth violence and related factors:

Juvenile justice information
Federal Bureau of Investigation
Criminal Justice Information Services Division
Phone: 304-625-4995
Web site: www.fbi.gov
Provides reported crime and arrest data.

Juvenile Justice Clearinghouse
Phone: 800-638-8736 or 301-519-5500

Justice Statistics Clearinghouse
Phone: 800-732-3277 or 301-519-5500

National Archive of Criminal Justice Data—ICPSR
P.O. Box 1248
Ann Arbor, MI 48106
Phone: 800-999-0960 or 313-763-5010
Web site: www.icpsr.umich.edu/nacjd
    Offers public use data files of many justice data sets.

National Center for Juvenile Justice
710 Fifth Ave.
Pittsburgh, PA 15219-3000
Phone: 412-227-6950
Web site: www.ncjj.org
    Provides juvenile court data and analyses of state juvenile code
    statutes.

National Criminal Justice Reference Service
P.O. Box 6000
Rockville, MD 20849-6000
Web site: www.ncjrs.org

Office of Juvenile Justice and Delinquency Prevention
810 Seventh St., NW
Washington, DC 20531
Phone: 202-307-5929
Web site: www.ojjdp.ncjrs.org

Office of National Drug Control Policy
Drug Policy Information Clearinghouse
Phone: 800-666-3332 or 301-519-5500

Other data on youth-related issues
    Bureau of Labor Statistics
    Postal Square Building, Room 2850
    2 Massachusetts Ave., NE
    Washington, DC 20212-0001
    Phone: 202-606-5886
    Web site: www.bls.gov

Centers for Disease Control and Prevention
National Center for Chronic Disease Prevention and Health Promotion
4770 Buford Highway, NE
Atlanta, GA 30341-3717
Web site: www.cdc.gov/nccdphp/dash/yrbs/ov.htm
    Provides data from the Youth Risk Behavior Surveys.

Centers for Disease Control and Prevention
National Center for Health Statistics
Division of Vital Statistics
6525 Belcrest Rd.
Hyattsville, MD 20782
Phone: 301-436-8500
Web site: www.cdc.gov/nchs
    Provides teen pregnancy data and mortality statistics.

Centers for Disease Control and Prevention
National Center for Injury Prevention and Control
Division of Violence Prevention
4770 Buford Highway, NE
Atlanta, GA 30341-3717
Web site: www.cdc.gov/ncipc/dvp/yvpt/yvpt.htm
    Offers data on violence by children and adolescents, including
    school violence and dating violence.

National Center for Education Statistics
555 New Jersey Ave., NW
Washington, DC 20208
Phone: 800-424-1616 or 202-219-1828
Web site: www.nces.ed.gov

National Clearinghouse on Child Abuse and Neglect Information
330 C St., SW Washington, DC 20447
Phone: 800-394-3366 or 703-385-7565
Web site: www.calib.com/nccanch
    Provides information on child maltreatment.

National Clearinghouse on Families and Youth
P.O. Box 13505
Silver Spring, MD 20911-3505

Phone: 301-608-8098
Web site: www.ncfy.com
  Offers information on runaways and homeless youth.

General- and special-population data
Bureau of the Census
Customer Services
Washington, DC 20233-8300
Phone: 301-457-4100
Web site: www.census.gov
  Provides wide range of data on the American public, including race
  and ethnicity, language use, poverty, marital status, education, and
  employment.

Office of Minority Health Resource Center
P.O. Box 37337
Washington, DC 20013-7337
Phone: 800-444-6472 (TDD 301-589-0951)
Fax: 301-589-0884
Web site: www.omhrc.gov
  Offers resources and referrals on minority health issues.

Chapter 2

STRATEGIES TO PREVENT YOUTH VIOLENCE

Best practices are the elements and activities of intervention design, planning, and implementation that are recommended on the basis of the best knowledge currently available.

INTRODUCTION

Youth violence is a complex public health problem with many risk factors, including individual beliefs and behaviors such as early aggression and use of alcohol or other drugs; family characteristics such as spousal abuse and lack of parental supervision; peer and school influences such as associating with delinquent friends; and environmental factors such as access to firearms. This complexity presents many challenges for those who are working to prevent youth violence (Dahlberg 1998).

This chapter discusses four distinct strategies for combating the problem of youth violence and offers for each strategy best practices—the elements and activities of intervention design, planning, and implementation that are recommended on the basis of the best knowledge currently available. Identified through extensive literature reviews and interviews with experts, these best practices will guide you in developing interventions that meet your community's and participants' needs and fit your goals and objectives. They will help you engage the community in your effort, hire and train an intervention staff, and locate resources and partners. They will also help you determine the time frame for your intervention, support and encourage your staff, and keep participants interested and engaged. And they will direct you in monitoring your intervention's progress and evaluating its final outcome.

The goal of this chapter—and of the sourcebook overall—is to share the experiences of others who have implemented interventions to prevent youth violence. In addition to the best practices for each strategy, we have included an *Additional Resources* section. We encourage you to contact the organizations listed and to review the publications described to learn what works particularly well and what barriers and problems may exist for interventions of interest to you. You may also want to review the studies listed in each strategy's reference section (the first strategy includes references for this introduction).

A NOTE ABOUT THE BEST PRACTICES

Ideally, best practices are based on knowledge derived from rigorous evaluations of interventions reported in peer-reviewed literature. However, a number of factors complicate this approach to identifying best practices for youth violence prevention efforts.

First, because the field of research in youth violence prevention is young, few longitudinal and randomized-control studies have been conducted. Second, while studies have evaluated the outcome of interventions, they have not typically evaluated the effectiveness of individual implementation practices. Therefore, the majority of best practices presented in this sourcebook are based on the hands-on, empirical observations of intervention practitioners and evaluators.

Because youth violence is such a high-priority public health concern, and because it may be years until we can report a significant number of science-based best practices, we felt it was important to include in this sourcebook promising intervention practices as well as scientifically proven ones.

PARENT-AND FAMILY-BASED STRATEGY

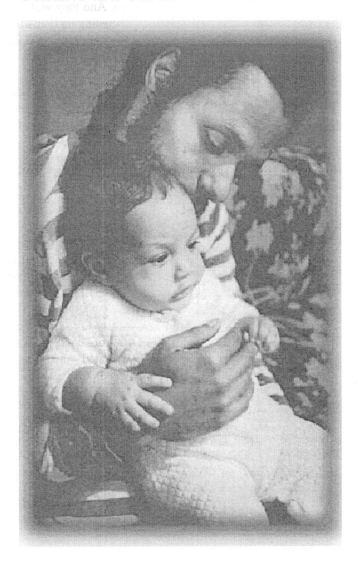

Parent- and family-based interventions are designed to improve family relations.

Overview of the Parent- and Family-Based Strategy

Parents' interactions with each other, their behavior toward their children, and their emotional state have been shown to be important predictors of children's violent behavior (Webster- Stratton 1997). Hendrix and Molloy (1990), for example, found that poor interactions between a mother and a child at age 1 year predict behavioral problems and aggression at age 6. Having an emotionally distressed parent at age 4 years has been found to contribute to a child's developing conduct disorders and antisocial behaviors (Buka and Earls 1993). Marital conflict and a lack of communication between parents have also been identified as risk factors for youth violence (Biglan and Taylor 2000; Buka and Earls 1993; Tolan and Guerra 1994).

Parent- and family-based interventions are designed to improve family relations. There is growing evidence that these interventions, especially those that start early and recognize all the factors that influence a family, can have substantial, long-term effects in reducing violent behavior by children. Parent- and family-based interventions combine training in parenting skills, education about child development and the factors that predispose children to violent behavior, and exercises to help parents develop skills for communicating with their children and for resolving conflict in nonviolent ways. This type of intervention is ideal for families with very young children and for at-risk parents with a child on the way.

Best Practices of Parent- and Family-Based Interventions

While the evidence base for parent and family interventions is growing, there is a need for more evaluation research. Those interventions that have been evaluated have typically not set violence reduction as an outcome measure. More commonly, they have measured reductions in delinquent behaviors, conduct disorders, or drug use, all of which are considered precursors to violence.

Despite the need for more evaluation, however, we have learned many lessons about what works using this strategy. This section offers the best practices of parent- and family-based interventions, combining recommendations by experts with general conclusions found in a review of the literature. We have organized the best practices around the steps involved in planning, implementing, and evaluating an intervention (see Chapter 1 for a review of those steps).

Identify the Populations You Want to Reach

Parenting interventions are generally more successful if they are implemented with the unique characteristics and needs of the intended participants clearly in mind. Before you develop your intervention, identify the group you want to reach.

At-Risk Populations

Substantial research has been devoted to identifying factors within the family unit that put a child at risk for developing violent behaviors. These factors may be related to behaviors and characteristics of either the parents or the child.

Parents' Risk Factors

Some risk factors that parents possess are dramatic and obvious, such as criminal and violent behavior, alcohol and other drug abuse, child abuse, and child neglect. Other, more subtle predictors include harsh or inconsistent discipline, lack of emotional interaction between the parent and child, and lack of parental supervision (Patterson, Reid, and Dishion 1992; Buka and Earls 1993). Many other behaviors, although not related directly to parenting, are also associated with children's violent behavior. Examples include lack of communication between spouses, marital conflict and divorce, parental social isolation, and parental depression or stress (Buka and Earls 1993; Tolan and Guerra 1994).

> *Avoid identifying socioeconomic status only as the determinant of risk. The perception that an intervention targets individuals simply because they are poor is highly stigmatizing.*

One study found that poor, single mothers—faced with many challenges and stressors—are at highest risk for developing parenting patterns that can lead to violent behavior by their children (Patterson, Reid, and Dishion 1992). Parents whose first language is not English often exhibit risk factors resulting from acculturation conflicts. And targeting low-income families has been shown to reduce child abuse and neglect (Campbell and Taylor 1996).

Avoid identifying socioeconomic status only as the determinant of risk. The perception that an intervention targets individuals simply because they are poor is highly stigmatizing. Find non-pejorative ways to identify people at different levels of risk.

Children's risk factors

Research has found that children at risk for violence can be identified by the time they are 3 years old (Olweus 1978). Factors that put children at risk include living in neighborhoods where violence commonly occurs, witnessing severely violent acts, being a victim of abuse, and associating with "rough" or antisocial peers. Other less obvious factors have also been associated with the development of violent behaviors. These include learning problems, a history of absenteeism from school, and frequent visits to the school counselor. A sudden change in behavior can also signal the beginning of violent tendencies.

High-Risk Populations

Some children are considered to be at high risk for developing violent behaviors. These children already exhibit clear behavioral markers of violent activity, including the following:

- bullying other children or being the target of bullies
- exhibiting aggressive behavior or being alternately aggressive and withdrawn
- being truant from school
- being arrested before age 14
- belonging to delinquent or violent peer groups
- abusing alcohol or other drugs
- engaging in antisocial behavior, such as setting fires and treating animals cruelly

Young Children (10 Years and Under)

The effectiveness of parenting interventions seems to increase exponentially when children are very young, before antisocial or aggressive behaviors are fully developed (Webster-Stratton and Hancock 1998; Webster-Stratton and Spitzer 1996). By the time a child reaches adolescence, both the child and the parents are following well-established patterns and are more resistant to long-term change (Patterson, Reid, and Dishion 1992; Taylor and Biglan 1998). And a 14-year-old boy relies much less on his family and is much more susceptible to external influences than a 7-year-old boy (Hendrix and Molloy 1990).

Expectant Parents

The earlier in a child's life a parent-based intervention begins, the greater the likelihood it will be effective. With this fact in mind, you may want to consider targeting parents who are expecting a child. Previous research suggests that intervening with a mother during the latter part of pregnancy and continuing with intervention activities during the first few years of her child's life can significantly reduce the risk of conduct disorder and violence (Olds 1997).

Consider the Cultural and Demographic Context of Intended Participants

When selecting your intended participants, consider their location, age, life circumstances, ethnicity or race, and needs. Try to select a group of people who live near each other and are alike in key characteristics. By targeting a group that is fairly homogeneous, you can better tailor materials and activities so they are more meaningful to participants.

Selecting a homogeneous group increases the likelihood that participants will form support groups and friendships that extend beyond the environment of the intervention. Such an outcome was achieved by the Houston Parent-Child Development Center, which targeted low-income, Mexican American parents (Johnson 1988).

You can also meet the needs of your participants more effectively when participants are alike. Wood and Baker (1999) developed a questionnaire to examine parent preferences, behaviors, and beliefs toward school-based parent-education programs among 395 low-income, culturally diverse parents from two elementary schools. Results indicated that parents of low socioeconomic status wanted to participate in parent-education events, but they were less likely than parents with higher levels of education to attend events at school. The greatest barriers to their participation were difficulty in getting time off from work (27%), cost (27%), lack of transportation (21%), and inability to find or afford babysitting (18%).

The earlier in a child's life a parent-based intervention begins, the greater the likelihood it will be effective.

Make sure your setting is conducive to interactive exercises and discussions.

Select an Appropriate Setting

The setting for a parenting intervention will likely be a school, community center, church, or other location where a group of people can meet. Make sure your setting is conducive to interactive exercises and discussions.

To reach people who live in remote areas or who have difficulty getting to and from an intervention site, you may need to bring the intervention to them. For example, in remote and rural areas in South East Queensland, Australia, a self-directed intervention delivered by telephone contact and written information was implemented (Connell, Sanders, and Markie-Dadds 1997). Twenty-four preschool children with problem behaviors and their families were recruited for a randomized, controlled study of the parenting intervention. Participants assigned to the intervention read sections of a book on parenting weekly for 10 weeks, completed tasks in the accompanying workbook, and participated in weekly telephone consultations (lasting up to 30 minutes) with a therapist. Parents were prompted to monitor their own and their child's behavior, set goals for behavior change, select strategies, identify strengths and areas for improvement, and select contingent rewards for themselves and their children. Results indicated that this self-directed, minimal intervention increased parents' perception of competency; reduced dysfunctional parenting practices; reduced disruptive behavior by the child; and significantly reduced mothers' feelings of anxiety, depression, and stress. Improvements in child behavior and parenting practices achieved at the end of the intervention were maintained at follow-up four months later.

Another self-directed intervention is Parenting Adolescents Wisely, a CD-ROM-based program. It was successfully implemented in Appalachia, where participants had little or no computer literacy (Olds 1997). Because the skill-building exercises require no orientation or supervision by staff, they can be conducted at any time, in locations most convenient to participants (Kacir and Gordon 1999). This intervention has also been successful with teen mothers and clinic-referred teens and parents (Lagges 1999; Segal 1995). With no other intervention or support, the rate of problem behaviors for children in the intervention dropped by half at one, three, and six months after their mothers participated in the intervention.

Involve the Community and Parents in Planning the Intervention

Organizations sponsoring parent- and family-based interventions should participate in developing the intervention. This involvement will help them feel ownership of the intervention so they are more likely to support its objectives, commit to evaluating outcomes, and hold themselves accountable for the impact of the intervention.

Parents also need to participate in the development process. The more active a role parents play in an intervention from its inception, the greater their sense of empowerment and accountability both during and after the intervention. Parents can also provide unique insight to help practitioners more closely tailor the intervention to participants' needs and priorities.

Set Clear Goals and Objectives for Intervention Outcomes and Implementation

Set clear, specific, observable goals and objectives for each intervention. They will help you evaluate an intervention's effectiveness and give parents and staff a sense of day-to-day accomplishment. Make sure goals and objectives are behavior-based and outcome-oriented—for example, reducing school truancy by 50 percent or establishing and keeping a weekly family budget. If you are modeling your intervention after one that has been proven effective, use the original intervention's evaluation framework to shape your goals and objectives.

Involve parents in setting objectives. Have them outline, with the practitioner's guidance, what they think their family can achieve and in what time period. Starting this kind of new initiative may seem overwhelming to parents: they are being asked to change the way they parent their child, even the way they conduct their daily affairs. Setting clear, definable goals enhances parents' sense of control and accountability (McMahon et al. 1996).

Select the Best Intervention for Your Participants and Develop Appropriate Materials

The intervention you select must be appropriate for the ages of the participants' children, the degree of violent behavior or level of risk for such behavior, and participants' cultural characteristics. It must also take into account family dynamics (how members interact with one another), the external environment (e.g., schools, housing), and the family's financial situation.

> *If you are modeling your intervention after one that has been proven effective, use the original intervention's evaluation framework to shape your goals and objectives.*

Consider the Children's Ages

A child's age influences many factors of parenting, from nurturing to discipline. For example, parents of a young child should set limits for their child's behavior, but with an older child, parents may want to negotiate those limits. Therefore, the contents of your intervention will be driven, in part, by the age of the children.

Young Children (Ages 10 and Under)

Interventions for parents of young children often have the best chance of effecting long-term, positive change because the behavior patterns of both parents and children have not been firmly established; they are still fairly malleable (Taylor and Biglan 1998). When developing an intervention for parents of preschool- and elementary school-age children, include an overview of child development so participants can set realistic, age-appropriate expectations about their children's behavior.

The following are other principles to include in an intervention for parents of young children:

- Playing with the child versus directing the child
- Praise and rewards for positive behavior and correction of undesired behavior
  - ➤ In order to change a child's behavior, positive reinforcement must be accompanied by appropriate, consistent, measured discipline of undesired behavior (Taylor and Biglan 1998).
- Decisions appropriate for children to make and those which should be made by the parents
- Supervision and discipline
  - ➤ Children need a consistent set of rules to follow, and parents need to discipline children in nonviolent ways when they break those rules.
- Influence of caregivers on children's beliefs, attitudes, and behaviors
- Effect of seeing violence, both in person and on television and film

One intervention that has worked well in families with young children is Parent-Child Interaction Training. In this intervention, low-income African American parents of preschool children with behavior problems attended five two-hour, small-group sessions composed of instruction, role playing, and supervised play sessions. After one year, children in the experimental group showed less aggression, hostility, anxiety, and hyperactivity than children in the control group (Strayhorn and Weidman 1991).

Adolescents and Teens

For parents of adolescents and teens, an intervention should explain appropriate developmental issues, including sexuality, growing independence, and the likelihood of rebellious behavior. Curricula for parents with older children should also discuss the following:

- Reframing the underlying motives for a child's behavior in non-pejorative terms (e.g., belonging, competence, reducing fear)
- Increasing positive and decreasing negative communication patterns among immediate family members, extended family, and peers
- Improving parents' ability to identify positive role models among extended family and the community and to minimize negative influences

The Adolescent Transition Program is one intervention that has been proven effective for families with older children. Designed for parents of middle-school students at risk for substance use, academic failure, and antisocial behavior, this intervention seeks to improve seven classic parenting skills: making neutral requests, using rewards, monitoring, making rules, providing reasonable consequences for rule violations, problem solving, and active listening. Classes are conducted weekly for 12 weeks in groups of eight to 16 parents and follow a skill-based curriculum. In a randomized control trial of the program, which involved 303 families over a four-year period, participants were compared with parents on a three-month waiting list. Parents in the program reported a lower tendency to overreact to their child's behavior, greater diligence in dealing with problem behavior, and less depression. There was also some indication of lower levels of daily antisocial behavior from the child. The more sessions a parent attended (many did not complete the 12- week program), the greater the reported improvements in behavior. We should note, however, that this evaluation is limited because it was based on the parents' assessment and interpretation of behavior rather than on objective measures (Irvine, Biglan, Smolkowski, Metzler, et al. 1999; Irvine, Biglan, Smolkowski, and Ary 1999).

Research has demonstrated the effectiveness of working with parents who are at increased risk for raising antisocial children.

Don't be Afraid to Target High-Risk Families

Many parents whose children have already displayed antisocial behaviors or have committed delinquent acts live in a stressful and isolating environment. Such parents may be economically distressed and socially cut off, with little access to financial or psychological support. The common belief is that it's extremely difficult to implement effective parent-training programs for disadvantaged parents, particularly low-income single mothers. However, this perception is misleading. Interventions that involve parents in planning, recruitment, group leadership, and priority setting have successfully enlisted and retained low-income participants, have positively influenced parenting behaviors, and have enhanced family and community support networks (Webster-Stratton 1998).

Violence prevention research on high-risk populations has demonstrated the effectiveness of working with parents who, because of socioeconomic and psychological factors—such as low income, single motherhood, or a history of abuse—are at increased risk for raising antisocial children. Several interventions have investigated the effectiveness of providing high-risk parents with parent training before or immediately after the birth of a child. These initiatives were designed to help parents manage their children and their lives more effectively and reduce the stress typically experienced by parents in the first few years of a child's life. The interventions offered a range of services: parent counseling, strategies for problem-solving, training in parenting techniques, and help in developing social support systems. Some even covered the children's childcare and healthcare expenses. One example of such an intervention has been offered by the Houston Parent-Child Development Center, which serves as a "parent college" for Mexican American families. Up to eight years after the intervention, children of participating parents had a lower incidence of reported problem behaviors in school than did control children (Johnson 1988).

Interventions for Parents of Delinquent Children

Many parents of children with serious behavior problems use ineffective disciplinary techniques. For example, parents of delinquent children tend to be inadequately involved in monitoring their child's day-to-day activities, to be inconsistent in applying discipline, and to display marginal levels of involvement in such areas as the child's academic progress (Dishion, Patterson, and Kavanagh 1992; Buka and Earls 1993; Bank et al. 1991). Often, a destructive pattern of "coercive interaction" exists between the child and the parents, characterized by a cycle of the child misbehaving and the parents threatening the child (Patterson, Reid, and Dishion 1992). While this reaction by the parents may be effective in the short-term, it promotes further aggression by the child in the long run. The first step in breaking this cycle is to change the parents' tactics and teach them alternative responses to their child's negative actions.

The coercion model is one intervention that can break this cycle. It involves eight family groups who participate in 12 weekly sessions, each lasting 90 minutes. The group sessions are supplemented with four individual family sessions. This model teaches parenting-behavior skills such as monitoring children's actions, fostering pro-social behavior, disciplining without aggression, and problem-solving through exercises, role play, and group discussion. Various evaluation procedures over time have shown this model to be effective in reducing problem behaviors and increasing family unity (Patterson, Reid, and Dishion 1992).

Another effective intervention for families with chronically delinquent children was developed by the Oregon Social Learning Center (OSLC). In this study, 55 families of boys who had multiple arrest histories and had committed at least one offense deemed "serious" by the court were assigned to either the OSLC parenting-training intervention or to a community treatment group involving 90-minute family-therapy sessions for approximately five months. Parents in the OSLC group were taught to monitor, record, and react to the daily behavior of their boys. Parents and children developed behavior contracts that specified pro-social and antisocial behavior and the positive and negative consequences that would result. Each family received an average of 21.5 hours of therapy and 23.3 hours of phone contact. Families were free to contact intervention staff for "booster shots" of support after the treatment year.

A significant reduction in arrests was achieved for both the intervention and the control group. However, the OSLC treatment produced results more quickly and with one-third less reliance on incarceration. The researchers state that the main outcome of the treatment may have been to help the parents remain actively involved and responsible for the conduct of their boys. We should note that researchers found the clinical work with these families to be extraordinarily difficult, and it took tremendous effort to prevent staff burnout (Bank et al. 1991).

Parents who abuse their children need to build nurturing skills as alternatives to their abusive parenting behaviors and attitudes.

Interventions for Abusive Parents

Parents who abuse their children need to build nurturing skills as alternatives to their abusive parenting behaviors and attitudes. The Nurturing Parenting Programs, family-centered interventions based on a re-parenting philosophy, teach those skills. Parents and children attend separate groups that meet concurrently. Cognitive and affective activities are designed to build self-awareness, positive self-concept/self-esteem, and empathy; teach alternatives to yelling and hitting; enhance family communication and awareness of needs; replace abusive behavior with nurturing; promote healthy physical and emotional development; and teach appropriate role and developmental expectations. Thirteen different interventions address specific age groups (infants, elementary school-age children, and teens), cultures (Hispanic, Southeast Asian, African American), and needs (special learning needs, families in alcohol recovery).

The initial Nurturing Program for Parents and Children 4 to 12 Years was extensively field-tested with 121 abusive adults and 150 abused children. Significant improvements were found in the attitudes of both parents and children, in personality characteristics of both parents and children, and in patterns of family interaction. Evaluations of subsequent nurturing programs have shown similar results (Bavolek 1996).

Empower Parents

A fundamental principle of effective parenting interventions is empowering parents to deal with their children. Parents— especially those of delinquent children—tend to feel out of control in many aspects of their lives. They may feel demoralized, frustrated, or depressed by their inability to parent effectively (Dishion, Patterson, and Kavanagh 1992). Interventions should increase parents' sense of self-control and self-efficacy, giving them confidence in their interactions with their children and making them feel accountable in a positive way for improvements in their children's behavior (Prinz and Miller 1996).

One way to empower parents is to give them information that will help them understand and react appropriately to their children's behavior. Interventions should provide training on how to nurture and communicate effectively with children, negotiate family rules and consequences, praise and reward children for pro-social behavior, and discipline without violence. They should teach parents effective means of punishment, such as "time outs" and loss of privileges, that do not promote aggressive interactions between parent and child.

Another empowering technique is to encourage parents to participate in the problem-solving process (Cunningham 1996). For example, in a collaborative group-therapy model used at the University of Washington Parenting Clinic, the therapist solicits parents' ideas, feelings, and information about their cultural background. In this model, therapists and parents feel joint ownership of solutions and outcomes (Webster-Stratton and Herbert 1994). In Los Niños Bien Educados, a program targeting Latino American families, participants were asked to define important cultural concepts about parenting. Participants defined what "bien educados" meant to them and recalled the cultural proverbs that were used in their own and their grandparents' homes (Alvy and Rubin 1981).

You can also build in activities to involve and empower parents, to make them feel that they are vital contributors to the intervention. For example, have parents bring refreshments to meetings, have them monitor their family's progress, or enlist participants to lead pep rallies.

Consider Cultural and Demographic Issues

Some participant groups have cultural beliefs or behaviors that present unique challenges for practitioners. Identify cultural issues up front and design intervention materials to address them. Culturally relevant content promotes a strong sense of group ownership, ethnic identity, community-building, and advancing one's group as a whole (Alvy 1994).

The Effective Black Parenting Program is a cultural adaptation of a generic parenting skill-building intervention called Confident Parenting (Alvy and Rubin 1981). This program reduced parental rejection, improved the quality of family relations, and reduced child behavior problems among African American families living in South Central Los Angeles. Key intervention components, in addition to skill building, included discussions contrasting "traditional" discipline (e.g., punishment, spanking) with "modern" self-discipline (internalized standards of effective behavior); discussion and reinforcement of issues related to "pride in blackness"; and the use of a black achievement perspective to link the life goals the parents had for their children with the abilities and characteristics the children need to achieve them (Myers et al. 1992).

Among some families of low socioeconomic status, parents' low level of education can make traditional communication channels ineffective. To address this challenge, program planners have developed interventions that de-emphasize written materials and verbal teaching methods, opting instead for role-playing and modeling techniques (Knapp and Deluty 1989).

> *To achieve long-term effects, interventions must also address the context in which parenting takes place.*

For many groups, interactive teaching techniques are most effective. These techniques incorporate not only didactic teaching but methods such as role-playing and problem-solving exercises. However, some parents prefer didactic authority figures and mistrust overly friendly strangers. With these groups, a practitioner would want to begin with a more formal style and ease into interactive teaching methods to avoid being viewed as disrespectful.

Address Environmental and Financial Concerns

Interventions that focus solely on parents' behavior may not result in changes that parents can sustain in the environment outside the intervention. To achieve long-term effects, interventions must also address the context in which parenting takes place. Today, the most successful interventions have been expanded to help parents improve their "life skills" and help them deal with issues such as social isolation, stress, depression, marital conflict, housing, and money matters. The general principle behind these broad interventions is that parents who are better able to manage everyday life issues will have the physical, psychological, and social resources to parent more effectively.

A variety of interventions integrate parenting life skills. One of the most researched, Henggeler's Multisystemic Therapy Program operates on the premise that a family is an interconnected unit in which a series of individuals (parent, child, siblings, extended family members) and external factors (work, school, housing situation) interact with one another to create an ongoing family dynamic (Borduin et al. 1990). Intervention activities are designed for each family on the basis of the family's risk and protective factors.

In a series of randomized control trials, in a variety of settings, the multisystemic approach has been successful. A study in Simpsonville, North Carolina, involved adjudicated youths who had at least one violent offense. After 59 weeks, the youths who received the multisystemic therapy (MST) had significantly fewer arrests (.87 versus 1.52) and fewer weeks incarcerated (5.8 versus 16.2) than youths receiving the usual services. The MST intervention families also reported improved family cohesion. A study in Columbia, Missouri, compared MST with individual therapy (IT) among 17-year-old multiple offenders and their families. At 5-year follow-up, MST youths were less likely to be arrested again, the families receiving MST reported and showed more positive changes in their overall family environment, and the MST parents showed greater reductions in psychiatric symptoms (Henggeler et al. 1996). MST was also found to be effective in the treatment of adolescent sexual offenders. Youths in the MST group had significantly fewer subsequent arrests for sexual crimes than did youths in the IT group (Borduin et al. 1990).

Select Staff Appropriate For Your Intervention

With the parent- and family-based strategy, the quality of the relationship between the practitioner and the parent can profoundly affect the outcome of your intervention. Therefore, your staff must be selected with great care, keeping in mind both the needs and desires of participants and the requirements of your intervention.

The persons best suited for parent-training intervention have the following characteristics:.

- Commitment to the intervention's objectives
- Experience with family interventions
- First-hand knowledge about the community (they either live or work there)
- Good interpersonal communication skills
- Knowledge of group dynamics
- Ability to manage resistance from participants

In addition, staff members should live near enough to participants to allow for frequent contact. They must also be available to work during the times that are most convenient to participants, usually during evenings and weekends. It may be helpful to select staff members who have characteristics like those of participants. For example, you could pair single mothers with staff who are also single mothers or African American participants with staffers of the same race. The Strengthening Families Program finds it effective to match therapists with parents as similar as possible in age, social standing, and cultural background (Kumpfer, Molgaard, and Spoth 1996).

Consider involving alumni of previous interventions to help bridge the gap between the practitioners and parents and to provide parents with support from someone who's "been there." Patterson's Coercion Model, for example, involves parent alumni as mentors to participating parents; the Strengthening Families Program hires parent alumni to support and reassure participants in an attempt to reduce drop-outs (Dishion, Patterson, and Kavanagh 1992; Kumpfer, Molgaard, and Spoth 1996).

The quality of the relationship between the practitioner and the parent can profoundly affect the outcome of your intervention.

Train Staff Members

In successful parenting interventions, the practitioner must form a bond of trust, respect, and collaboration with parents (Taylor and Biglan 1998; Johnson 1988; Webster-Stratton and Spitzer 1996; Prinz and Miller 1996). Training for your intervention should prepare staff members to play the role of teacher, supporter, and facilitator.

In addition to teaching your staff how to carry out the activities of your intervention, training should include information about child-rearing principles, participants' values, and other cultural and religious beliefs that may affect how parents interact with their children or with intervention staff. It should also show staff members how to employ an interactive teaching method, engaging participants in group discussions and role playing exercises; this technique is more effective than a formal, didactic style. Provide staffers with a training manual they can refer to throughout the intervention.

Recruit Families

To recruit participants for your parenting intervention, work with community groups, churches, mental health facilities, law enforcement agencies, and schools in your area. Get involved personally in the recruitment process. Phone or visit parents at home or speak with them in public places, communicating to them that you understand and respect the challenges they face. Consider hiring or assigning administrative or public-relations staff to assist with recruitment. When targeting high-risk families, you may need to enlist the help of a community gatekeeper—for example, a trusted school official, community elder, or minister—to facilitate referrals.

You may need to offer parents incentives to encourage participation, especially if you are targeting at-risk parents. You are, after all, asking them to commit to making profound changes, something parents may not enter into lightly. Think about what would entice parents, such as money, transportation fare (subway, bus, taxi), food, or free childcare. Ask local businesses to contribute products and services that would interest intended participants.

Implement Your Intervention

How you implement your intervention will depend on many factors, including the activities planned and the participants involved. However, the following principles apply to any parenting intervention:

- Schedule activities at times and locations that are convenient to parents.
- Give staff appropriate titles—that is, if your intervention is not therapy, per se, refer to staff members as session leaders, practitioners, facilitators, or instructors rather than therapists.
- Build on the knowledge parents already have.
- Minimize lectures; maximize interactive teaching opportunities.

- Make sure staffers model the behaviors being taught (e.g., effective listening skills, non-aggressive reactions to conflict).
- Offer opportunities for parents to ask questions, offer feedback, and practice the skills taught.
- Implement all components of an intervention that has been proven effective. Using only selected components may not produce the results of the original intervention.

It may help to explain the behavioral theories that underlie the parenting techniques being taught. For example, parents are much more likely to persevere in using recommended disciplinary tactics, particularly when they do not result in immediate improvements in their child's behavior, if they have a good overall understanding of the behavioral principles on which the tactics are based.

Intervention Delivery May Vary Depending on Children's Ages and Families' riSk Factors

The age of the children in participating families will affect delivery techniques. What works for parents with very young children may not be as effective for parents with older children.

Young Children (10 Years and Younger)

For interventions designed to influence families with young children, group-based parenting interventions (ideally, with seven to nine families) have been shown to be as effective as one-on-one training, and they are more cost-effective (Webster- Stratton 1984). Another method that has worked with families of preschoolers and elementary school-age children is the Parent-Child Interaction Training Program, which teaches parents productive behaviors and strategies for interacting with their children. It includes supervised individual play sessions between parent and child that give parents an opportunity to test their new skills.

> *Implement all components of an intervention that has been proven effective. Using only selected components may not produce the results of the original intervention.*

The following techniques have also been effective among this age group:

- Home visits that supplement group sessions

- Self-administered video training combined with a brief, two-session consultation
- Videotapes that present models of effective parenting techniques (provided participants are able to identify with the characters portrayed) and vignettes of ineffective techniques

At-Risk and High-Risk Older Children

For interventions reaching parents of at-risk older children, the following formats—used individually or in combination—are most effective:

- Group sessions with parents only
- Individual family therapy
- Group sessions with multiple families

Helping parents contact one another and engage in activities outside of regularly scheduled training sessions can help maximize your intervention's results.

For families with high-risk older children—especially children with multiple risk factors—individualized and home-based family interventions are most effective. Interventions for these families should:

- Address logistical challenges;
- Adhere to a clearly-defined format;
- Enlist the support of groups that can help reinforce desired behaviors.

When working with high-risk families, it is essential to link parenting interventions to child-based interventions that actively involve the child at risk. The Multisystemic Therapy Program, for instance, develops ongoing strategies and goals for every relevant member of the family. It requires the child to perform certain tasks and follow certain behaviors, and it requires the parent to monitor and reward or discipline the child's actions (Henggeler et al. 1996).

Use the Full Range of Parent-Training Activities

The most effective parent- and family-based interventions include a variety of activities, including multi-session classes for small groups, one-day seminars for large groups, video and audiotape training materials, self-instruction activities, and home projects to implement skills.

A number of studies have demonstrated the success of videotape modeling as a mechanism for educating parents and stimulating discussion. While video-based interventions can be effectively self-administered, the best results are obtained when the video is combined with group interactions (Webster-Stratton, Kolpacoff, and Hollinsworth 1988). In five randomized studies with more than 500 families, an intervention incorporating the videotape modeling and parent-group discussions resulted in greater reductions in child conduct problems and more significant improvements in parents' disciplinary approaches and parent-child interactions than did one-on-one parent training, discussion groups without videotape modeling, or videotape modeling without discussion (Webster-Stratton 1996).

Additional research has been conducted on early interventions with videotape modeling using the BASIC and ADVANCE Parent Training Videotape Modeling interventions, the PARTNERS 1 Academic Skills Training intervention for parents, the PARTNERS 2 intervention for teachers, and the KIDVID Child Social Skills and Problem-Solving Training intervention for children ages 3 to 8. Although interventions with self-administered activities alone did reduce conduct difficulties, better results were achieved when interventions also included parent training in interpersonal and coping skills (Webster- Stratton 1996).

The Functional Family Therapy (FFT) model combines assessment, therapy, and education to address dysfunctional communication styles in families with delinquent children (Alexander and Parsons 1982). In the assessment phase, therapists evaluate family behavior patterns and gather information about problem behaviors. The therapy phase is designed to change attitudes, expectations, emotional reactions, and perceptions to reduce blame among family members. The education phase teaches skills in family communication, relationship building, and problem solving; reinforces positive interactions and manages conflict; and teaches parents how to reward and reinforce pro-social behavior.

Parenting patterns are hard to change—there are no "quick fixes."

In a number of controlled studies, FFT has been shown to modify dysfunctional communication and reduce rates of delinquency among treated youths and their siblings (Barton et al. 1985). Gordon and colleagues (1988) replicated the FFT model in a group of 54 rural, economically disadvantaged juvenile offenders in southeastern Ohio. Half of the group was non-randomly assigned to receive in-home FFT from psychology graduate students. Most of this group had committed multiple serious offenses and had been assigned to family therapy by the court. A control group of 27 lower-risk delinquent youths received only probation services. After 2½ years, recidivism rates were 11 percent in the treatment group and 67 percent in the comparison group. A later study that measured changes in the group at the end of an additional 32-month period (after the subjects had become adults) found recidivism rates of 9 percent for misdemeanor and felony offenses in the treatment group and 41 percent in the comparison group (Gordon, Graves, and Arbuthnot 1995).

Set a Realistic Time Frame for Your Intervention

Parenting patterns are hard to change—there are no "quick fixes." Expect your intervention to take at least several months. A desirable duration for interventions targeting at-risk families is approximately 22 sessions; 12 sessions is typically appropriate for families not considered at risk.

In most cases, sessions should occur at regular intervals (e.g., weekly or biweekly) and last for no more than two hours. Longer sessions have been successful in some programs, as long as frequent breaks were provided. Formats involving out-of-home group sessions should be convenient in terms of childcare, transportation, and the availability of food.

Support Intervention Staff to Prevent Burnout

Parent- and family-based interventions can be challenging and emotionally taxing for the intervention staff. It is critical that you provide staffers with support and encouragement. Staff members need coaching and consultation regularly and should be given plenty of opportunities to talk with a supervisor about how well they are meeting the intervention objectives as well as about personal, job-related objectives. Consider hiring staff on a part-time basis or making intervention implementation a component of a full-time position. This may help prevent staff burnout. It is also beneficial to provide staff members with flexible schedules.

Encourage Participants to Stay Involved

Parent- and family-based interventions can last for many months with results that are subtle and gradual. You will need to maintain participants' interest in your intervention and keep them focused on the long-term goal. In addition to offering incentives like free food, transportation, and childcare, plan events that will entice parents to complete the intervention. For example, hold graduation ceremonies or provide gift certificates as a reward for completion.

Monitor Progress and the Quality of the Implementation

As your intervention moves along, monitor activities to be sure they are being carried out as planned. This is especially important if you are implementing an evaluated intervention— you need to follow all steps to make sure you achieve the same results.

The following steps will help you determine if your intervention is on track:

- Base staff supervision on outcomes.
- Record accomplishments as they occur.
- Track attendance to sessions.
- Have someone who is not involved in delivery of the intervention perform spot-checks of activities.
- Have parents keep a log of what kind of activities and information were delivered.
- Gather additional feedback from parents and staffers that can help you fine tune the intervention.

Evaluate Outcomes

From the beginning, consider how to evaluate the outcome of your intervention. Have participants assess changes in their own behavior and that of their children. The intervention staff should also evaluate those changes. You can use a third party to identify changes, as well. For example, review school records of children whose families participated in the intervention to see if rates of delinquent behavior or absenteeism have dropped.

Expect Setbacks

Behavior change does not happen overnight. Long-standing family issues, crises, and disciplinary problems cannot be cured with a single treatment. Set realistic expectations for your intervention and let parents know that obstacles and setbacks will occur along the way (Taylor and Biglan 1998). Informing parents that they will probably face resistance and recurring behavior problems from their children will better prepare them for these difficulties so they can remain committed to the intervention (Prinz and Miller 1996).

> *From the beginning, consider how to evaluate the outcome of your intervention.*

Maintain Results After Implementation

Without the guidance and support of intervention staff, participants may find it difficult to keep momentum going after the intervention ends. You can take some steps to maintain the positive results of your intervention after it has been completed.

For example:

- Provide a follow-up source for parents to call with questions and concerns.
- Offer "booster" sessions.
- Help parents form support groups.
- Refer parents to resources for marital and financial help.
- Link parents with organizations that can reinforce the values and behaviors taught by your intervention.
- Tie your intervention with the activities of other relevant community groups (such as civic and religious groups), parks and recreation activities, and school programs.

Follow-up activities, conducted several months or more after the original intervention has ended, can also increase the long-term benefits of your effort. These activities can be especially effective when targeting families with young children. Buka and Earls (1993) likened violence prevention strategies to immunization: a "vaccination" at an early age followed by periodic "booster sessions" throughout childhood and adolescence. Scheduling follow-up activities to coincide with difficult developmental periods, such as a child's initial entry into school or transition to a new school (for example, moving from elementary to middle school), can be particularly helpful in addressing behavioral problems. And involving practitioners and staff members from the original intervention can lend continuity to activities.

Link Parent- and Family-Based Interventions with Other Strategies

While parent-based interventions are among the most effective strategies known thus far for preventing violence by children and adolescents, once children reach school age it is essential to complement this strategy with one that addresses the influence of factors outside the home (Taylor and Biglan 1998; Brestan and Eyberg 1998).

Negative academic and social experiences in school can result in a child's developing violent behavior or associated risk factors.

Evidence has shown that a partnership between parents and the school is more effective than parent-based strategies alone (McMahon et al. 1996; Webster-Stratton 1993; Coleman 1997). A coordinated effort among parents, teachers, school psychologists, and school nurses can identify problems early so practitioners can intervene with programs to teach problem-solving, develop conflict-resolution skills, and enhance academic skills (Honig 1999; Schweinhart 1999).

Summary

The relationship between parent and child can play a profound role in the child's development of violent behavior or behaviors shown to be precursors of violence. Parent- and family-based interventions have proven highly effective in preventing such behaviors, especially when they address families' environmental, cultural, and financial needs and are paired with other interventions based in the school or community.

REFERENCES

Alexander JF, Parsons BV. *Functional Family Therapy: Principles and Procedures.* Carmel, CA: Brooks/Cole, 1982.

Alvy KT. Parent Training Today: *A Social Necessity.* Studio City, CA: Center for the Improvement of Child Caring, 1994: 23-30.

Alvy KT, Rubin HS. "Parent Training and the Training of Parent Trainers." *Journal of Community Psychology* 1981;9:53-66.

Bank L, Hicks JM, Reid JB, Patterson GR, Weinrott MR. "A Comparative Evaluation of Parent-Training Interventions for Families of Chronic Delinquents." *Journal of Abnormal Child Psychology* 1991;19(1):15-33.

Barton C, Alexander JF, Waldron H, Turner CW, Warburton J. "Generalizing Treatment Effects of Functional Family Therapy: Three Replications." *American Journal of Family Therapy* 1985;13(3):16-26.

Bavolek SJ. *Research and Validation Report of the Nurturing Programs.* Park City, UT: Family Development Resources, Inc., 1996.

Biglan A, Taylor TK. "Why We Have Been More Successful at Reducing Tobacco Use Than Violent Crime." *American Journal of Community Psychology* 2000;28(3):269-302.

Borduin CM, Henggeler SW, Blaske DM, Stein RJ. "Multisystemic Treatment of Adolescent Sexual Offenders." *International Journal of Offender Therapy and Comparative Criminology* 1990;34(2):105-113.

Brestan EV, Eyberg SM. "Effective Psychosocial Treatments of Conduct-Disordered Children and Adolescents: 29 Years, 82 Studies, and 5,272 Kids." *Journal of Clinical Child Psychology* 1998;27(2):180-189.

Buka S, Earls F. "Early Determinants of Delinquency and Violence." *Health Affairs* 1993;Winter:46-64.

Campbell FA, Taylor K. "Early Childhood Programs that Work for Children from Economically Disadvantaged Families." *Young Children* 1996;51(4):74-80.

Coleman M. "Families and Schools: In Search of Common Ground." *Young Children* 1997;52(5):14-21.

Connell S, Sanders MR, Markie-Dadds C. "Self-Directed Behavioral Family Intervention for Parents of Oppositional Children in Rural and Remote Areas." *Behavior Modification* 1997;21(4):379-408.

Cunningham CE. "Improving Availability, Utilization, and Cost Efficacy of Parent Training Programs for Children With Disruptive Behavior Disorders." In: Peters RD, McMahon RJ, editors. *Preventing Childhood Disorders, Substance Abuse, and Delinquency.* Thousand Oaks, CA: Sage Publications Inc., 1996: 144-160.

Dahlberg LL. "Youth Violence in the United States: Major Trends, Risk Factors, and Prevention Approaches." *American Journal of Preventive Medicine* 1998;14(4):259-272. (This article was referenced in the introduction to Chapter 2.)

Dishion TJ, Patterson GR, Kavanagh KA. "An Experimental Test of the Coercion Model: Linking Theory, Measurement, and Intervention." In: McCord J, Tremblay RE, editors. Preventing Antisocial Behavior: *Interventions from Birth Through Adolescence.* New York: The Guilford Press, 1992: 253-282.

Gordon DA, Arbuthnot J, Gustafson KE, McGreen P. "Home- Based Behavioral-Systems Family Therapy with Disadvantaged Juvenile Delinquents." *American Journal of Family Therapy* 1988;16(3): 243-255.

Gordon DA, Graves K, Arbuthnot K. "The Effect of Functional Family Therapy for Delinquents on Adult Criminal Behavior." *Criminal Justice and Behavior* 1995;22(1):60-73.

Hendrix K, Molloy PJ. *Interventions in Early Childhood.* Background paper prepared for the Forum on Youth Violence in Minority Communities: Setting the Agenda for Prevention; 1990 Dec 10-12; Atlanta (GA).

Henggeler S, Cunningham PB, Pickrel SG, Schoenwald SK, Brondino MJ. "Multisystemic Therapy: An Effective Violence Prevention Approach for Serious Juvenile Offenders." *Journal of Adolescence* 1996;19(1): 47-61.

Honig AS. *Longitudinal Outcomes from the Family Development Research Program.* Paper presented at the Biennial Conference of the Society for Research in Child Development; 1999 Apr 16; Albuquerque (NM).

Irvine AB, Biglan A, Smolkowski K, Metzler CW, Ary DV. "The Effectiveness of a Parenting Skills Program for Parents of Middle School Students in Small Communities." *Journal of Consulting and Clinical Psychology* 1999;67(6):811-825.

Irvine AB, Biglan A, Smolkowski K, Ary DV. "The Value of the Parenting Scale for Measuring the Discipline Practices of Parents of Middle School Children." *Behaviour Research and Therapy* 1999;37(2): 127-142.

Johnson DL. "Primary Prevention of Behavior Problems in Young Children: The Houston Parent-Child Development Center." In: Price RH, Cowen EL, Lorion RP, Ramos-McKay J, editors. *14 Ounces of Prevention.* Washington, D.C.: American Psychological Association, 1988: 44-52.

Kacir C, Gordon D. "Parenting Adolescents Wisely: The Effectiveness of an Interactive Videodisk Parent Training Program in Appalachia." *Child and Family Behavior Therapy* 1999;21(4):1-22.

Knapp PA, Deluty RH. "Relative Effectiveness of Two Behavioral Parent Training Programs." *Journal of Clinical Child Psychology* 1989;18(4):314-322.

Kumpfer KL, Molgaard V, Spoth R. "The Strengthening Families Program for the Prevention of Delinquency and Drug Use." In Peters RD, McMahon RJ, editors. *Preventing Childhood Disorders, Substance Abuse, and Delinquency.* Thousand Oaks, CA: Sage Publications, Inc., 1996: 241-267.

Lagges A. "Use of an Interactive Laserdisc Parent Training Program With Teenage Mothers." *Child and Family Behavior Therapy* 1999;21(1): 19-37.

McMahon RJ, Slough NM, Conduct Problems Prevention Research Group. "Family-Based Intervention in the Fast Track Program." In: Peters RD, McMahon RJ, editors. *Preventing Childhood Disorders, Substance Abuse, and Delinquency.* Thousand Oaks, CA: Sage Publications, Inc., 1996:90-110.

Myers HF, Alvy KT, Arrington A, Richardson MA, Marigna M, et al. "The Impact of a Parent Training Program on Inner-City African-American Families." *Journal of Community Psychology* 1992;20(2):132-147.

Olds DL. "Prenatal/Early Infancy Project: Fifteen Years Later." In: Albee GW, Gullotta TP, editors. *Primary Prevention Works.* Thousand Oaks, CA: Sage Publications, Inc., 1997: 41-67.

Olweus D. "Stability of Aggressive Reaction Patterns in Males: A Review." *Psychological Bulletin* 1979;86(4):852-875.

Patterson GR, Reid JB, Dishion TJ. *A Social Interactional Approach IV: Antisocial Boys.* Eugene, OR: Castalia Publishing, 1992.

Prinz RJ, Miller GE. "Parental Engagement in Interventions for Children at Risk for Conduct Disorder." In: Peters RD, McMahon RJ, editors. *Preventing Childhood Disorders, Substance Abuse, and Delinquency.* Thousand Oaks, CA: Sage Publications, Inc., 1996: 161-183.

Schweinhart LJ. *Generalizing from High/Scope Longitudinal Studies.* Presentation at the Biennial Conference of the Society for Research in Child Development; 1999 Apr 15-18; Albuquerque (NM).

Segal D. *Parenting Adolescents Wisely: Comparing Interactive Computer-Laserdisc and Linear-Video Methods of Intervention in a Parent-Training Program.* Unpublished doctoral dissertation, Ohio University (Athens), 1995.

Strayhorn JM, Weidman CS. "Follow-up One Year after Parent- Child Interaction Training: Effects on Behavior of Preschool Children." *Journal of the American Academy of Child and Adolescent Psychiatry* 1991;30(1):138-143.

Taylor TK, Biglan A. "Behavioral Family Interventions for Improving Childrearing: A Review of the Literature for Clinicians and Policy Makers." *Clinical Child and Family Psychology Review* 1998;1(1): 41-60.

Tolan P, Guerra N. *What Works in Reducing Adolescent Violence: An Empirical Review of the Field.* Boulder, CO: The Center for the Study and Prevention of Violence, University of Colorado at Boulder, 1994.

Webster-Stratton C. "Parent Training with Low-Income Families: Promoting Parental Engagement through a Collaborative Approach." In: Lutzker JR, editor. *Handbook of Child Abuse Research and Treatment.* New York: Plenum Publishers, 1997: 183-210.

Webster-Stratton C. "Early Intervention for Families of Preschool Children with Conduct Problems." In: Guralnick MJ, editor. *The Effectiveness of Early Intervention: Second Generation Research.* Baltimore, MD: Paul Books, 1997: 429- 454.

Webster-Stratton C. "Early Intervention with Videotape Modeling: Programs for Families of Children with Oppositional Defiant Disorder or Conduct Disorder." In: Hibbs ED, Jensen PS, editors. *Psychosocial Treatments for Child and Adolescent Disorders: Empirically Based Strategies for Clinical Practice.* Washington, DC: American Psychological Association, 1996: 435-474.

Webster-Stratton C. "Strategies for Helping Early School-Aged Children With Oppositional Defiant and Conduct Disorders: The Importance of Home-School Partnerships." *School Psychology Review* 1993;22 (3):437-457.

Webster-Stratton C. "Randomized Trial of Two Parent-Training Programs for Families with Conduct-Disordered Children." *Journal of Consulting and Clinical Psychology* 1984;52(4):666- 678.

Webster-Stratton C, Hancock L. "Training for Parents of Young Children with Conduct Problems: Content, Methods, and Therapeutic Processes." In: Briesmeister J, Schaefer CE, editors. *Handbook of Parent Training: Parents as Co-Therapists for Children's Behavior Problems.* New York: John Wiley & Sons, Inc., 1998: 98-152.

Webster-Stratton C, Herbert M. *Troubled Families—Problem Children: Working with Parents Who Have Children With Conduct Disorders: A Collaborative Process.* New York: John Wiley & Sons, Inc., 1994.

Webster-Stratton C, Kolpacoff M, Hollinsworth T. "Self- Administered Videotape Therapy for Families with Conduct- Problem Children: Comparison with Two Cost-Effective Treatments and a Control Group." *Journal of Consulting and Clinical Psychology* 1988;56(4):558-566.

Webster-Stratton C, Spitzer A. "Parenting a Young Child with Conduct Problems: New Insights Using Qualitative Methods." In: Ollendick TH, Prinz RJ, editors. *Advances in Clinical Child Psychology.* New York: Plenum Publishers, 1996; 1-62.

Wood WD III, Baker JA. "Preferences for Parent Education Programs Among Low Socioeconomic Status, Culturally Diverse Parents." *Psychology in the Schools* 1999;36(3):239-247.

ADDITIONAL RESOURCES ON PARENT-
AND FAMILY-BASED INTERVENTIONS
TO PREVENT YOUTH VIOLENCE

The following intervention summaries have been adapted from information listed on the Strengthening America's Families web site, a project funded by the Office of Juvenile Justice and Delinquency Prevention. Further details about the interventions are available at www.strengthening families.org and from the contact person provided with each description. This listing is provided as a service to readers, but the presence of an intervention on this listing does not imply endorsement by CDC or the Department of Health and Human Services.

Bethesda Family Services Foundation

This foundation provides comprehensive individual and family-centered treatment to children ages 10 to 18 who were referred by the court as a result of delinquent offenses (referral to the program is in lieu of jail time). The intervention provides treatment for the entire family during nontraditional hours. Youths receive at least six months of treatment, and parents attend meetings and training sessions. Dominic Herbst, President

P.O. Box 210
West Milton, PA 17886
Phone: 570-568-2373
E-mail: staff@bfsf.org

Birth to Three

This education intervention for parents with infants and young children strives to strengthen families and prevent child abuse. A variety of interventions is offered, including the Infant Program (a five-month parenting-confidence curriculum), Making Parenting a Pleasure, and Teen Parents.

Minalee Saks, Executive Director
86 Centennial Loop
Eugene, OR 97401
Phone: 541-484-5316
E-mail: birthto3@efn.org
Web site: www.efn.org/~birthto3

CEDEN Health and Fair Start Program

The Center for Development, Education, and Nutrition provides comprehensive services to strengthen families in need of prenatal, early childhood, and parenting education. The Health and Fair Start Program serves primarily low socioeconomic status families and children younger than five years who have developmental delays.

Terry Aruguello, Program Coordinator
1208 East 7th St.
Austin, TX 78702
Phone: 512-477-1130
E-mail: CEDEN@bga.com

CICC's Effective Black Parenting

Created to meet the needs of African American parents, the Center for the Improvement of Child Caring fosters effective family communication, family values and identity, and healthy self-esteem. It provides basic parenting strategies taught by black educators and mental health professionals using a culturally appropriate curriculum.

Kerby T. Alvy, Ph.D., Director
Center for the Improvement of Child Caring
11331 Ventura Blvd., Suite 103
Studio City, CA 91604-3147
Phone: 818-980-0903
E-mail: cicc@flash.net
Web site: www.ciccparenting.org

Families and Schools Together Program

FAST is an intervention for at-risk children and adolescents ages 3 to 14. Its structure gives young people and their parents both a voice and a role in the prevention process. The intervention develops separate support networks for youths and parents, using a multi-family format, and brings them together for family activities.

Lynn McDonald, Ph.D.
11770 West Lake Park Dr.
Milwaukee, WI 53224
Phone: 800-221-3726
E-mail: mrmcdona@facstaff.wise.edu

Families in Focus

This family skills training intervention is designed to strengthen the family and prevent social and behavioral problems. The intervention was originally designed for high-risk youths ages 8 to 14 but has also been delivered to children of all ages. A Home Learning Guide and Family Profile Questionnaire help direct families to specific activities.

Mary Altizer, Administrative Assistant
Families Worldwide
75 East Fort Union Blvd.
Midvale, UT 84047
Phone: 801-562-6178
E-mail: maltize@homeplus.com

Family Support Program

This intervention uses case-management services to reduce juvenile delinquency among at-risk middle-school children and their families. Case-management services identify family needs and develop an individual plan for the family. Youths attend after-school groups and meet with coordinators individually. Family members attend workshops.

Chris Corallo, School Administrator
Middle School Rd.
Rocky Mount, VA 24151
Phone: 540-483-7209
E-mail: ccarallo@frco.k12.va.us

First Steps/Fremont County Family Center

First Steps offers comprehensive child development and parenting services for families with children from birth to 5 years. The intervention, which operates as part of the Fremont County Family Center, incorporates monthly home visits and play groups that are held four times a week for children, siblings, and parents.

Katherine Bair, Homevisiting Coordinator
1401 Oak Creek Grade Rd.
Canon City, CO 81212
Phone: 719-269-1523
E-mail: fcfc@ris.net

Focus on Families

This intervention focuses on families with parents who are addicted to drugs, enrolled in methadone treatment, and have children ages 3 to 14. Families participate in an orientation and then attend curriculum sessions for 16 weeks. Parent sessions are held in the mornings, and parents and children attend practice sessions in the evenings.

Kevin Haggerty, M.S.W.
Social Development Group
9725 3rd Ave., NW, Suite 401
Seattle, WA 98115
Phone: 206-685-1997
E-mail: haggerty@u.washington.edu

Functional Family Therapy

Functional Family Therapy is a family-based intervention for youths with problem behavior. Goals include improving family communication and supportiveness, identifying solutions to family problems, and developing behavior change strategies. Therapists work with each family in a clinical setting or in-home treatment.

James F. Alexander, Ph.D.
1329 Behavioral Science
University of Utah
Salt Lake City, UT 84112
Phone: 801-581-6538
E-mail: jfafft@psych.utah.edu

Health Start Partnership and CARES Parenting Program

This intervention fosters secure mother-infant attachments by encouraging responsive parenting. For two years, cohorts of eight to 12 women with infants participate in home visits and weekly support and education groups. The program also provides medical care, lunch, and transportation.

Gloria Ferguson, Team Leader
491 West University Ave.
St. Paul, MN 55103-1936
Phone: 612-221-4368
E-mail: gloria.j.ferguson@healthpartners.com

Helping the Noncompliant Child
Helping the Noncompliant Child is designed for parents and their children ages 3 to 8 years with conduct disorders. Its long- term goals are prevention of serious conduct problems and juvenile delinquency in young children. Parenting skills are taught through demonstration, role-playing, and direct practice.

Robert J. McMahon, Ph.D.
University of Washington
Department of Psychology
Box 351525
Seattle, WA 98195-1525
Phone: 206-543-5136
E-mail: mcmahon@u.washington.edu

Home-Based Program: Coordinated Children's Services Initiative
The Coordinated Children's Services Initiative serves families of children with emotional and behavioral disabilities. Individualized care plans are developed with the family's needs in mind. The parent-training components focus on behavior modification.

Roberta Karant, Ph.D.
790 Park Ave.
Huntington, NY 11743
Phone: 516-854-9199

Home-Based Behavioral Systems Family Therapy
This intervention, based on the Functional Family Therapy model (discussed previously), reaches families with lower educational levels and higher levels of pathology than did the original model. The intervention is delivered in five phases, with increasing involvement of therapists. Its long-range goal is to reduce juvenile delinquency and teen pregnancy.

Donald A. Gordon, Ph.D.
Psychology Department
Ohio University
Athens, OH 45701
Phone: 740-593-1074
E-mail: gordon@ohiou.edu

HOMEBUILDERS

This intervention aims to strengthen the family and prevent foster care and out-of-home placement. It includes four to six weeks of intensive, in-home services to children and families. A practitioner provides counseling and services and is on call for crisis intervention.

Charlotte Booth, Executive Director
Behavioral Sciences Institute
181 South 333rd St., Suite 200
Federal Way, WA 98003-6307
Phone: 253-874-3630
E-mail: bsihomebuilders@wordnet.att.net

Home Instruction Program for Preschool Youngsters

HIPPY's goals include preventing academic underachievement by increasing literacy in the home and empowering parents to be educators and advocates for their children. The weekly intervention for economically disadvantaged parents and preschool-age children includes role-playing and other activities.

Barbara Gilkey
Arkansas Children's Hospital
800 Marshall Street, Slot 651
Little Rock, AR 72202
Phone: 501-320-3727
E-mail: bgilky@exchange.ach.uams.edu

The Incredible Years: Parent, Teacher, and Children Series

The Incredible Years offers support and problem-solving to parents of children ages 3 to 12. In the Parent Training Series, parents meet in groups with a trained leader to foster support, problem-solving, and self-management. The Teacher Training Series prepares teachers to present the separate Child Training Series.

Carolyn Webster-Stratton, Ph.D.
The Incredible Years
1411 8th Ave., West
Seattle, WA 98119
Phone: 206-285-7565
888-506-3562

E-mail: incredibleyears@seanet.com
Web site: www.incredibleyears.com

MELD

This parent education intervention uses peer support groups to help parents develop skills and confidence. MELD reaches out to parents of preschool children and has been adapted to address parents who are single, are of Hispanic and Southeast Asian descent, are deaf and hard-of-hearing, or have children with special needs.

Joyce Hoelting
123 North 3rd St., Suite 507
Minneapolis, MN 55401
Phone: 612-332-7563
E-mail: meldctrl@aol.com

Multisystemic Therapy Program

MST offers intensive family-based treatment to address determinants of serious antisocial behavior in adolescents and their families. General goals are to reduce rates of antisocial behavior and out-of-home placements and to empower families to resolve future difficulties. Individual treatment goals are developed in collaboration with the family.

Scott Henggeler, Ph.D., Director
Department of Psychiatry and Behavioral Sciences
Family Services Research Center
Medical University of South Carolina
Box 250861
67 President St., Suite CPP
Charleston, SC 29425
Phone: 843-876-1800
E-mail: henggesw@musc.edu

NICASA Parent Project

The NICASA Parent Project was designed to meet the needs of working parents of children from birth through adolescence. The intervention, presented at work sites during lunch time, focuses on child development, balancing work and family, and improving parenting skills.

Joyce Millman, Director of Parent Services
Northern Illinois Council on Alcoholism and
Substance Abuse (NICASA)
31979 N. Fish Lake Rd.
Round Lake, IL 60073
Phone: 847-546-6450
E-mail: joycemil@ais.net

Nurturing Parent Programs

There are 13 Nurturing Parenting Programs designed for specific cultures, family dynamics, and children's age groups. The programs build nurturing skills to reduce abusive parenting, juvenile delinquency, alcohol abuse, and teen pregnancy. Parents and children attend separate groups that meet concurrently. Each program has been researched and validated as an effective intervention for the treatment and prevention of child abuse and neglect.

Stephen Bavolek, Ph.D.
27 Dunnwoody Court
Arden, NC 28704-9588
Phone: 828-681-8120
E-mail: fdr@familydev.com
Web site: www.familydev.com

Parenting Adolescents Wisely

PAW is a self-administered interactive CD-ROM-based intervention designed for parents who are unfamiliar with computers. Parents view scenes of common family problems, choose a solution, and listen to a critique. The intervention helps families enhance relationships and decrease conflict while enhancing child adjustment.

Donald A. Gordon, Ph.D.
Psychology Department
Ohio University
Athens, OH 45701
Phone: 740-593-1074
E-mail: gordon@ohiou.edu
Web site: www.familyworksinc.com

Parents Anonymous

Parents Anonymous welcomes parents who are concerned about their parenting ability and seek support, information, and training. Parents set the agenda for each weekly two-hour meeting. Complementary children's interventions are offered concurrently. Basic parenting skills are discussed, and members offer 24-hour support to parents.

Teresa Rafael, M.S.W., Vice President of Programs
Parents Anonymous, Inc.
675 W. Foothill Blvd., Suite 220
Claremont, CA 91711-3475
Phone: 909-621-6184
E-mail: parentsanon@msn.com
Web site: www.parentsanonymous-natl.org

Preparing for the Drug Free Years

An intervention for parents of children in grades 4 through 8, PDFY seeks to reduce drug abuse and behavioral problems in adolescents by increasing parents' skills. The intervention focuses on family relations and conflict resolution and incorporates behavioral skills training and communication approaches to parent training.

Barbara McCarthy
130 Nickerson St., Suite 107
Seattle, WA 98109
Phone: 800-736-2630
E-mail: sales@drp.org

Project SEEK

Services to Enable and Empower Kids (SEEK) serves children ages 0 to 11 who have a parent in prison. SEEK's goal is to break the intergenerational cycle of criminality. The program includes home visits; advocacy and referral; support groups for children, adolescents, and caregivers; and communication with the inmate.

Carol Burton, Program Director
806 Tuuri Place
Flint, MI 48503
Phone: 810-767-5750
E-mail: burton@mottchc.org

Raising a Thinking Child: I Can Problem Solve (ICPS) Program for Families

ICPS develops a set of interpersonal cognitive problem-solving skills for children up to age 7. The program's goal is to prevent more serious problems by addressing behavioral predictors early in life. Parents learn a problem-solving style of communication that guides young children to think for themselves.

Myrna Shure, Ph.D.
MCP/Hahnemann University
245 N. 15th St., ADD MS625
Philadelphia, PA 19102-1192
Phone: 215-762-7205
E-mail: mshure@drexel.edu

Strengthening Families Program

A family-skills training intervention, SFP was designed to reduce risk factors for substance use and other problem behaviors in high-risk children of substance abusers, but it has also been used widely with parents who are not substance abusers. The intervention addresses families with children 6 to 10 years old and provides classes for parents, children, and families.

Karol L. Kumpfer, Ph.D.
University of Utah, 215 HPER-N
Salt Lake City, UT 84112
Phone: 801-581-8498
E-mail: karol.kumpfer@hsc.utah.edu

The Strengthening Families Program for Parents and Youth 10 to 14

The long-term goal of this intervention is to reduce substance use and behavior problems during adolescence. Intermediate goals include improved child management skills among parents and improved interpersonal and pro-social skills among youths. Parents and adolescents attend separate skill-building groups and also spend time together in supervised family activities.

Virginia Molgaard, Ph.D.
Iowa State University
Social and Behavioral Research
Center for Rural Health
2625 North Loop Dr., Suite 500

Ames, IA 50010
Phone: 515-294-8762
E-mail: molgaa@exnet.iastate.edu

Strengthening Hawaii Families

This intervention, based on cultural values, seeks to prevent problems such as substance abuse and domestic violence. It aims at increasing resiliency in both the community and family. A 14-session curriculum provides tools and a process for families and children 5 to 12 years old to build on existing family strengths.

Sandra Lacar
1130 North Nimitz Highway, Suite A-259
Honolulu, HI 96817
Phone: 808-545-3228

Strengthening Multi-Ethnic Families and Communities

This intervention reaches out to ethnically and culturally diverse parents of children 3 to 18 years old with the goal of reducing violence against self, family, and community. Parent-training classes are held at various community locations. The curriculum is delivered in 12 sessions of three hours each; materials are available in several languages.

Marilyn L. Steele, Ph.D.
1220 S. Sierra Bonita Ave.
Los Angeles, CA 90019-2552
Phone: 323-936-0343
E-mail: dr_mls@earthlink.net

Structural Family Therapy

This intervention for Hispanic and African American families addresses youths who abuse drugs and exhibit behavior problems. Therapists implement tailored activities to change negative patterns of family interactions and create opportunity for more functional interactions.

Victoria B. Mitrani, Ph.D.
1425 NW 10th Ave., 3rd Floor
Miami, FL 33136
Phone: 305-243-4592
E-mail: vmitrani@mednet.med.miami.edu

Treatment Foster Care

This parent-training intervention works with foster parents to provide placements for adolescents ages 12 to 18 who are referred because of chronic delinquency. Treatment foster parents implement a daily behavior management plan over the course of six months. The adolescents participate in weekly therapy, and their biological parents also receive treatment.

Patricia Chamberlain, Ph.D., Director
Oregon Social Learning Center
160 East Fourth
Eugene, OR 97401
Phone: 541-485-2711
E-mail: pattic@oslc.org

HOME-VISITING STRATEGY

Overview of the Home-Visiting Strategy

Violent and criminal behavior, poor mental health, drug use, and poor school performance have been linked to several childhood risk factors, including child abuse and neglect, poverty, a poor relationship with the parent(s), poor physical and mental health, parental drug or alcohol abuse, and child abuse and neglect (Wolfner and Gelles 1993; Oates et al. 1995; Krysik et al. 1997; Norton 1998). By eliminating these risk factors, we can help reduce the aggressive and violent behaviors we see in our schools and communities. Home visiting is one effective strategy to address these factors.

Home-visiting interventions bring community resources to at-risk families in their homes. During home visits, intervention staff provides information, healthcare, psychological support, and other services that participants need to function more effectively as parents. These programs have helped improve maternal health and pregnancy outcomes, increase employment and education among young parents, reduce reliance on welfare, improve children's injuries, and reduce criminal behavior by young people. This strategy is ideally implemented with families who are expecting or have recently had their first child.

> *Home-visiting interventions bring community resources to*
> *at-risk families in their homes.*

Best Practices of Home-Visiting Interventions

Although additional research is needed to evaluate the effectiveness of home-visiting interventions, several studies have revealed promising findings as well as techniques and principles for planning and implementing these efforts. This section presents the practices identified in those studies, along with recommendations from experts in the field of youth violence prevention.

Identify the Populations You Want to Reach

Many European countries provide home visits to all families, regardless of risk status. Some advocates have argued that this service should be made available to all families in the United States, as well. But home-visiting interventions are resourceintensive, and few communities have the financial and human resources needed to carry out an effective program on such a large scale. Therefore, targeting select groups for home-visiting services is typically most appropriate. A needs assessment conducted with input from the community will help identify families who could benefit most from a home-visiting intervention. Community leaders should play a key role in this decision, as they are often in a position to direct the allocation of resources.

Expectant Parents and First-Time Parents

Research suggests that home visiting has the greatest impact when it begins early in the parenting process. Therefore, homevisiting interventions often begin when participants are pregnant and continue through the first few years of the children's lives. Targeting first-time parents seems to be ideal, the rationale being that positive changes will carry over to future pregnancies and children. In addition, research indicates that mothers involved in a home-visiting intervention will likely have fewer unintended pregnancies (Olds and Kitzman 1990).

Olds and colleagues (1998) examined the long-term effects of prenatal and early-childhood home visits on children's antisocial behavior. They found that adolescents whose mothers had been visited by nurses expressed less antisocial behavior and had lower substance-use rates than did adolescents in a comparison group. Adolescents from the study group also reported significantly fewer instances of running away, fewer arrests, fewer convictions and violations of probation, fewer lifetime sex partners, fewer cigarettes smoked per day, and fewer days having consumed alcohol in the six months preceding the study.

Home visits seem to benefit high-risk families most.

Similar results were achieved by Aronen and Kurkela (1996). They studied the long-term effects of a home-based familycounseling intervention that took place during the first five years of the children's lives. Eighty families experienced 10 home visits per year; another 80 families served as a comparison group. Both groups included low-risk and high-risk families. Each child's mental-health status was assessed at age 15. Adolescents in the intervention families had significantly fewer mental health symptoms on child-behavior checklists filled out by their parents and on the youths' self-reports. The counseling predicted better mental health at year 15 for both high- and lowrisk families.

High-Risk Families

Although positive results have been achieved among both highand low-risk families, home visits seem to benefit high-risk families most. One study found that home-visiting interventions produce the greatest benefit when they are focused on single and adolescent parents living in communities with high poverty rates (Olds and Kitzman 1990; Olds et al. 1997). Interventions aimed at poor, unmarried mothers have been shown to improve the maternal life course, reduce the number of months that mothers relied on public assistance and food stamps, reduce behavioral problems associated with alcohol and other drug use, and reduce the number of arrests (Olds et al. 1997). Daro (1993) found that families exhibiting child abuse and neglect responded best to interventions incorporating home visits. One of the most important benefits reported for these families was the concrete assistance that visiting practitioners offered in resolving childcare problems such as discipline and toilet training.

Remember that, although home visits can bring about substantial changes in the long run, they can rarely bring about immediate changes in the environmental, financial, and psychological issues that high-risk families face. Long-term dedication is needed to affect social adversities such as unemployment, poverty, drug abuse, and malnutrition.

Other Groups

Young people who drop out of high school or show poor school engagement are at increased risk of becoming teen parents (Manlove 1998). As discussed previously, young, unwed parents are often at increased risk of developing parenting styles that are associated with the development of youth violence. And given that dropping out of school, poor academic performance, and a general lack of interest in school are, by themselves, risk factors for developing violent behavior, this group is an appropriate target for home visits. Parents with limited social support are also ideal participants in home-visiting interventions. These parents need help dealing with the stress of parenting and with other life stressors such as financial and marital difficulties or unemployment.

Generate Support in the Community

You will need a great deal of support from your community—in the form of both financial and human resources—to carry out a home-visiting intervention. To convince community members and leaders that your intervention is worth their time and money, show them how the intervention will meet the community's perceived needs and goals and explain the long-term benefits of early prevention efforts. Here are a few arguments for conducting a home-visiting intervention:

- Helping expectant mothers to stop using drugs or alcohol and to eat a better diet will improve the health and development of their babies.
- Improving parent-child interactions from the earliest possible time will help prevent abusive disciplinary tactics.

- Addressing parents' physical and emotional needs will increase their patience and tolerance, making them better able to nurture their children.

In addition to preventing the risk factors for violence, homevisiting interventions may save communities money down the road. Data on the cost-effectiveness of home visits are limited, and additional studies must be conducted (Barnett 1993), but a few cost analyses have revealed savings in government spending for food stamps and the Temporary Assistance for Needy Families Program (formerly the Aid to Families with Dependent Children Program).

Set Clear Goals and Objectives

Setting goals and objectives for home visits must be done on two levels. First, practitioners should identify the desired outcome of the intervention. For example, an overall goal might be to reduce the number of elementary school students who exhibit early warning signs of developing violent behavior, such as withdrawing from classmates and performing poorly in school.

Objectives, then, might be to improve the parent-child interactions in families of preschoolers and to help parents develop educational activities to better prepare their children for school.

> The interventions that succeed in helping at-risk families
> are intensive, comprehensive, and flexible.

On the second level, home visitors must help each family set its own goals and objectives. This will ensure a good balance between the intervention's goals and the family's needs. It will also help parents feel ownership of the intervention because they will be working toward something they feel is important to their family.

Design the Best Intervention for Your Participants

The activities and materials you develop for your home visits will depend on the characteristics and needs of the participants, your goals and objectives, and the expertise of the home visitors. Overall, the interventions that succeed in helping at-risk families are intensive, comprehensive, and flexible (Wallach 1994). The following principles will apply to all home-visiting interventions:

- Each component of a home-visiting intervention should build on or relate to the others; homevisit activities should be synergistic.
- Home visits should focus on the parent-child interaction and on the relationship between the parents.
- Home visitors should address the child's physical and mental health and development; activities should be appropriate for the child's age.
- Appropriate discipline techniques should be taught and appropriate behavior modeled by home visitors.

Home-visiting interventions should also help parents build support networks. By linking them to community organizations, churches, medical-care providers, and other services, home visitors can help parents obtain assistance with finances, emotional problems, and other needs.

For Expectant Mothers and Parents with Young Babies

In a randomized trial in Elmira, New York (a semi-rural community), Olds and Kitzman (1993) demonstrated the effectiveness of nurse home visits for first-time pregnant teens who were poor or unmarried. The home visits were designed to improve the mothers' health, help them develop effective parenting skills, and improve their financial situation by easing the transition into the work force after their children were born. The goal was to reduce problems resulting from poor prenatal health, dysfunctional caregiving, and financial difficulties caused by closely spaced pregnancies, lack of education, and inconsistent employment.

The study produced encouraging results. Compared with controls, nurse-visited women experienced greater social support—both from family and friends and from government and community services. They also smoked fewer cigarettes, had better diets, and suffered fewer kidney infections during pregnancy. Through age 2, children born to nurse-visited women were 80 percent less likely to be identified as victims of child abuse or neglect and were seen in hospital emergency departments 56 percent fewer times. Four years after delivery of the first child, the women in the intervention group had 42 percent fewer additional pregnancies and participated in the workforce at a rate 84 percent higher than that of the control group. The cost to the government for this intervention was recovered before the children's fourth birthdays (Olds et al. 1993).

A follow-up of the original Elmira study revealed that positive results endure (Olds et al. 1997; Olds et al. 1998). Fifteen years after the initial intervention, data showed a reduction from 90 months to 60 months of recourse to the Aid to Families with Dependent Children Program among low-income, unmarried mothers. The home visitation program was also replicated in Memphis, Tennessee, among a predominantly black population. Results, although smaller in magnitude, were similar to those obtained in the semi-rural, mostly white community. (Olds et al. 1999; Kitzman et al. 1999).

For Families with Evidence of Child Abuse or Maltreatment

Previous research suggests that the incidence of child abuse increases the odds of future delinquency and adult criminality by 40 percent (Widom 1992). A high percentage of juvenile sex offenders may have been victims of childhood violence themselves (Feindler and Becker 1994). Studies and interviews with experts have found home-visiting interventions to be effective in reducing the risk for and incidence of child abuse and maltreatment (Brust, Heins, and Rheinberger 1998; Carnegie Corporation 1994).

Wasik and Roberts (1994) conducted a survey of 1,904 homevisiting interventions, 224 of which stated their primary focus was to provide services for abused and neglected children and their families. More than three-quarters of respondents rated three key elements of home visits as being of primary importance—improved parent-coping skills, enhanced parenting skills, and emotional support. Stress management, enhanced child development, and child and family advocacy were also rated as high priorities by more than half of respondents.

A successful home-visiting program aimed at preventing child abuse and neglect is Hawaii's Healthy Start Program, established in 1985 as a demonstration project. It now reaches more than half of Hawaii's at-risk population. This program uses home visits to improve families' coping skills and functioning, promote positive parenting skills, foster healthy parent-child interactions, and promote optimal child development. Results of the initial three-year project were conclusive: not a single case of abuse occurred among the project's 241 high-risk families (Breakey and Pratt 1991, 1993).

The Healthy Start Program offers a systematic approach to preventing child abuse among at-risk infants and toddlers. This approach forms the foundation for programs developed through Healthy Families America (HFA), a partnership of Prevent Child Abuse America (formerly the National Committee to Prevent Child Abuse) and the Ronald McDonald House Charities. While each state has autonomy in designing and implementing its HFA programs, key components include the following (Daro and Harding 1999):

- systematic, hospital-based screening to identify high-risk families
- home visits to provide family support services
- individualized plans for continuing service based on family need and risk level
- linkage to medical services (e.g., immunization and well-baby check-ups)
- coordination with and referrals to other health, counseling, and social services

Results indicate that this approach reduces child abuse, somewhat improves the home environment, improves children's healthcare and development, and reduces reliance on public assistance (Krysik et al. 1997; Norton 1998). A list of state HFA contacts is included in the *Additional Resources* section for this strategy.

Select Staff Appropriate for Your Intervention

Home visits may be conducted by a variety of individuals— public-health or registered nurses, social workers, paraprofessionals, volunteers, and advocates and liaisons. For most home-visiting interventions, however, a health professional or paraprofessional specifically trained to make home visits will be best able to achieve the results desired.

Before you select your staff, develop a framework for your intervention that specifies the job roles and responsibilities of all staff members. Base hiring, training, and supervision on that framework. Be sure to hire staff members whose experience and educational background fit the requirements of your intervention. For example, if your objectives include improving the health of pregnant women and their babies, nurses will be most appropriate; on the other hand, if your aim is to improve the learning skills of preschoolers in participating families, you may need staff members with a teaching background.

Nurses

Public health nurses appear to be in a position to detect community problems and trends before other health care providers (Bekemeier 1995). They may be the best choice for your intervention's staff, especially if your intended participants are at-risk pregnant women.

The expertise nurses possess appears to be well accepted and even desired by most expectant parents because their focus is on health—first, that of the pregnant woman and later, that of the baby. In addition, families may feel more at ease in asking for help from a nurse than from social-service professionals or counselors because there is less of a potential stigma associated with nursing assistance. In fact, a pregnant woman's asking for nurse-related assistance may be viewed as a sign of her positive intentions toward her health and that of her baby. Nurses are also ideal home visitors because:

- they can deliver content that contains a lot of medical information;
- they are trained to teach, use good questioning techniques, detect subtle cues, set priorities, and manage cases;
- they have an accepted role in the lives of pregnant women that can facilitate early acceptance and trust.

Paraprofessionals

For some interventions, paraprofessionals—counselors, social workers, and specially trained community volunteers—will be effective home visitors. An intervention implemented as a randomized controlled trial in Denver, Colorado, compared the effectiveness of paraprofessionals and nurses in improving pregnancy outcomes, infant care, and parental life course. Overall, nurses produced a larger and broader range of beneficial effects: improved prenatal health behaviors, improved viability of the newborn, more effective infant care, increases in the children's language development, and decreased rates of subsequent pregnancy. However, paraprofessionals effected significant changes, as well. The environment of the homes visited by paraprofessional became more conducive to children's development (at 21 months); early postpartum participation in the workforce was achieved by women of low psychological resources; and women had lower rates of subsequent pregnancy. More studies are needed to determine under what circumstances paraprofessionals trained in home visiting can be most effective. Researching intended participants can help identify the kinds of paraprofessionals who are most likely to be trusted and accepted by families. With both nurses and paraprofessionals, the beneficial effects of home visits are attributable to the particular program model and to the protocols that guide their visits (Olds 1998).

> *Public health nurses may be the best choice for your intervention's staff.*

Staff Characteristics

Whether you employ nurses, paraprofessionals, or others, all staff members must be available to conduct home visits when it is most convenient for participants. Since welfare reform, more mothers are working and may only be available on weekends or evenings. Staffers must also be committed to the effort and must get to visits on time, attend every visit, and complete the intervention. To be successful, home-visiting interventions rely on the development of a trusting relationship between the participants and the visitors. Tardiness and inconsistent attendance erode that trust.

The following characteristics are also highly desirable for home visitors:

- motivation, self-confidence, and a good sense of humor
- empathy and an open mind
- an understanding of the principles of parenting and child development
- sensitivity to cultural customs and political issues
- good communication skills
- critical-thinking and problem-solving abilities
- ability to relate to people of diverse backgrounds

Special Considerations for Home Visitors

Because intervention staff will be going into participants' homes and discussing potentially sensitive issues, practitioners must consider several factors when selecting visitors and pairing them with participating families.

Confidentiality

Staff members must not be allowed to conduct visits in the homes of family members or friends. Participants may be reluctant to share with people they know details about problem behavior (e.g., child abuse, drug use) or concerns about their parenting abilities. All home visitors should sign an agreement of confidentiality to protect the privacy of the participants. However, practitioners should identify emergency circumstances in which home visitors may violate that agreement in order to help the family (e.g., when the health or safety of participants is endangered).

Male Home Visitors

Carefully assess the context and sensitivities of the intended participants before selecting men to be home visitors. Some fathers—in particular, single fathers—may be willing to participate in an intervention led by a man. However, other fathers may feel competitive or even hostile toward a male visitor. Many visits are conducted in homes where a father is not present. Single mothers may feel unsafe or uncomfortable with a male visitor. When male visitors are undesirable to your participants, try having them accompany the primary home visitor occasionally as an auxiliary with special expertise.

Cultural Issues

Matching the cultural background of a home visitor with that of the family may or may not be important. The preferences of your intended participants should dictate this decision. Regardless of the cultural background of the home visitor, he or she must portray a neutral orientation toward race, ethnicity, religion, and other cultural factors.

Train Staff Members

Training that prepares staff members for home-visiting work is essential, regardless of their prior education and experience. Practitioners should determine the core competencies staff will need to meet the intervention's goals and objectives and ask staff members to provide input about their training needs. At a minimum, the training curriculum should cover the following topics:

- protocol for home visits (what it's appropriate for visitors to do)
- pregnancy health, transition to motherhood, and parent-child bonding and attachment
- signs of and risk factors for child abuse and neglect
- developing a trusting relationship with participants
- setting goals and resolving disagreements
- steps for creating a safe home environment for children
- signs of and referral information for mental health problems, substance abuse, and domestic violence
- personal safety for the home visitor

You will probably need to engage in intensive outreach to bring families into your program.

In most cases, professional staff members (those with at least a 4-year college degree) should receive 80 hours of training; paraprofessionals should receive 200 hours. Provide opportunities for role playing so staffers can practice new skills and offer feedback. And develop a training manual to complement in-class activities and serve as a reference during implementation.

Recruit Participants

Participation in home-based interventions must be voluntary. In an ideal world, families would jump at the chance to participate in your intervention. But in reality, you will probably need to engage in intensive outreach to bring families into your program. Families may be reluctant to participate because they:

- feel insulted by the implication that they need help;
- view intervention staff as "the establishment";
- fear discovery of illicit activities;
- view visits as an invasion of privacy.

Additionally, new mothers may be tired or depressed and may not have the energy to engage. They may also feel they do not have time for visits.

Implement Your Intervention

Implementing home-visiting interventions poses complex challenges. Home visitors must address a variety of oftenchanging issues related to the families' circumstances. And in many cases, a long time period is required to achieve relatively small changes.

Match the Duration, Frequency, and Intensity of Your Intervention with Families' Needs

How long your intervention continues, how often visits occur, and how long each visit lasts will depend on the families' needs and the goals set for your effort (Brust, Heins, and Rheinberger 1998; Powell 1993). On average, home-visiting interventions last about one year; more intensive programs may run as long as three to five years. Home visits most commonly occur on a weekly basis. Monthly visits are the minimum for families with infants and very young children; for families of older children, quarterly visits may be appropriate if the intervention incorporates other forms of community support. Most visits last between 30 minutes and one hour, but they may run longer (Wasik and Roberts 1994).

The frequency of visits may decrease as families mature in the intervention, are successfully linked to needed services, and master the skills and information set forth in the intervention objectives. If parent-group meetings are part of the intervention, alternate the weeks of home visits with those of group meetings. Each visit should have a clear structure and set activities. To keep activities on track, focus on long-term goals. At the end of each visit, note progress and discuss how upcoming activities reflect mutual expectations. Creating a "contract" with participants might be useful in determining what should be achieved during each visit. While it's important to form a comfortable relationship with participants, visits should not become social gatherings. Also, the content of visits should not be driven by crises.

Encourage Participants to Stay Involved

Participants in home-visiting interventions often drop out. They may become discouraged when changes occur very slowly, or they may come to believe that they no longer need the services home visits provide (Olds and Kitzman 1993). Home visitors need to keep participants committed to the intervention. The following tips can help:

- Be flexible. Balance the need to follow delivery protocol with the family's objectives and circumstances.
- Resolve differences immediately. Listen carefully to participants' concerns and respect their points of view.
- Provide empowering feedback. Seek opportunities to reinforce parents' positive behavior, especially in bonding with a new baby or in responding to the baby's cues.
- Use video feedback. Film interactions between parents and child. Highlight the child's developmental milestones.
- Involve children in activities. Help parents identify family activities that are appropriate for the children's ages and interests.
- Involve other family members, but not so many or so often that the parent visitor dialogue is disrupted. Let participants define who "family" is.
- Schedule fun activities, such as singing, storytelling, and going to a park or community event.

While it's important to form a comfortable relationship with participants, visits should not become social gatherings.

Support Intervention Staff

To help prevent staff burnout, limit the caseloads of homevisiting staffers to no more than 15 families; in some communities, caseloads will be significantly smaller (HFA 1996). Strongly caution staff members against getting involved in family problems they are unqualified to handle. For example, home visitors should not play therapist if participants appear to be suffering from depression or other mental health problems. Families should be referred to community resources for crisis issues.

During implementation, provide your staff with ongoing opportunities for training and group discussions. Keep lines of communication open so staff members can approach supervisors with concerns or questions at any time. Supervisors should watch staff closely for signs of fatigue, discouragement, and difficulty with implementing activities.

Monitor Progress and the Quality of Your Intervention

As with any prevention effort, a home-visiting intervention must be monitored to make sure it is on schedule and on track. Collecting data throughout implementation can help you verify that activities are being carried out as planned and help you identify early problems in delivery that may jeopardize the intervention's success. The following suggestions should help you effectively monitor your effort:

- Supervise intervention staffers closely to make sure they are following the protocol for home visits.
- Have staff members record procedures as they are completed.
- Encourage participants to communicate concerns (e.g., if they feel their needs are not being met).
- Ask participants to keep a log of activities (every third visit is usually sufficient).
- Record qualitative observations as well as quantitative, but keep recording to a minimum so it does not become disruptive.
- Find out—through surveys, focus groups, or visits by supervisors— why drop-outs left the intervention. The data you gather may help you improve the intervention.

Review monitoring data frequently. Remember that no intervention goes exactly as planned. If procedures or activities are deemed ineffective or problematic, alter or discontinue them (Slaughter-Defoe 1993).

Evaluate Changes

To determine whether your intervention has met its goals, note changes in participants' behaviors and in family interactions as the intervention progresses. Compare them with baseline data established when implementation began to determine if the intervention resulted in positive outcomes. Have parents note improvements in their behavior and that of their children and in parent-child interactions. Parents can also evaluate their confidence in parenting and handling conflicts that occur in the home. Home visitors, especially nurses, can assess the health and development of the children, as well as evaluate the behavioral changes they observe. If the children attend school or a childcare program, teachers and caregivers can also provide data about the children's behavior.

Maintain Results after Implementation

To sustain the positive effects of the intervention, develop a strategic plan to help participants with the transition that occurs when the intervention ends. For example, you might schedule quarterly "boosters" or direct parents to community organizations that can provide support. Consider offering incentives such as diplomas and graduation ceremonies to foster transition.

Anticipate the need for follow-up interventions. Keep track of families after the initial intervention ends so it's easier to locate them. Sending Christmas cards and Mother's and Father's Day cards, for example, can help keep addresses current. By sharing success stories with funders and policy-makers, you can gain support for follow-up activities.

Link Home Visits with Other Strategies

Home visits are an effective component of programs seeking to prevent violence by young people, but they may not be sufficient on their own (Weiss 1993). Although more research is needed to test the hypothesis, combining early home-based interventions with school programs and other community efforts may be an effective strategy in preventing violence and other negative health outcomes.

Summary

Home-visiting interventions improve parenting skills, provide social support to families, recognize and manage behavior problems, and promote child health and development. These types of interventions are likely to have a far greater impact on delinquency and violence than secondary and tertiary prevention programs such as those of the criminal justice system (Rivara and Farrington 1995).

REFERENCES

Aronen E, Kurkela SA. "Long-Term Effects of an Early Home- Based Intervention." *Journal of the American Academy of Child and Adolescent Psychiatry* 1996;35(12):1665-1672.

Barnett WS. "Economic Evaluation of Home Visiting Programs." *Future of Children* 1993;3(3):93-112.

Bekemeier B. "Public Health Nurses and the Prevention of and Intervention in Family Violence." *Public Health Nursing* 1995;12(4):222-227.

Breakey G, Pratt B. "Healthy Growth for Hawaii's 'Healthy Start': Toward a Systematic Statewide Approach to the Prevention of Child Abuse and Neglect." *Zero to Three* 1991;11(4):16-21.

Breakey G, Pratt B. "Healthy Start Home Visiting: Hawaii's Approach." *The APSAC Advisor* 1993;6(4):7-8.

Brust J, Heins J, Rheinberger M. *A Review of the Research on Home Visiting: A Strategy for Preventing Child Maltreatment.* Anoka, MN: Health Care Coalition on Violence, February 1998.

Carnegie Corporation of New York. *Starting Points: Meeting the Needs of Our Youngest Children,* April 1994. Cited in *Healthy Families America. Perspective,* November 1994.

Daro D. "Child Maltreatment Research: Implications for Program Design." In: Cicchetti D, Toth SL, editors. *Child Abuse, Child Development, and Social Policy: Advances in Applied Developmental Psychology, Volume 8.* Norwood, NJ: Ablex Publishing Corp., 1993: 331-367.

Daro D, Harding K. "Healthy Families America: Using Research to Enhance Practice." *Future of Children* 1999;9(1):152-176.

Feindler EL, Becker JV. "Interventions in Family Violence Involving Children and Adolescents." In: Eron LD, Gentry JH, Schlegel P, editors. *Reason To Hope: A Psychosocial Perspective on Violence and Youth.* Washington, DC: American Psychological Association, 1994: 405-430.

Healthy Families America. *Critical Elements for Effective Home Visitor Services.* Chicago: National Committee to Prevent Child Abuse, February 1996.

Kitzman H, Olds DL, Sidora K, Henderson CR Jr, Hanks C, Cole R, et al. "Enduring Effects on Nurse Home Visitation on Maternal Life Course: A 3-Year Follow-up of a Randomized Trial." *Journal of the American Medical Association* 1999;283(15):1983-1989. Krysik J, LeCroy CW, Ashford JB, Milligan K. *Healthy Families Arizona: Evaluation Report 1992-1996.* Phoenix: Arizona Department of Economic Security, December 1997.

Manlove J. "The Influence of School Dropout and School Disengagement on the Risk of School-age Pregnancy." *Journal of Research on Adolescence* 1998;8(2):187-220.

Norton DR. *Healthy Families Pilot Program: State of Arizona Office of the Auditor General Annual Evaluation*, January 1998.

Oates RK, Gray J, Schweitzer L, Kempe RS, Harmon RJ. "A Therapeutic Preschool for Abused Children: The Keepsafe Project." *Child Abuse and Neglect* 1995;19(11):1379-1386.

Olds DL, Kitzman H. "Can Home Visitation Improve the Health of Women and Children at Environmental Risk?" *Pediatrics* 1990;86(1):108-116.

Olds DL, Kitzman H. "Review of Research on Home Visiting for Pregnant Women and Parents of Young Children." *Future of Children* 1993;3(3):53-92.

Olds DL, Henderson CR Jr, Phelps C, Kitzman H, Hanks C. "Effects of Prenatal and Infancy Nurse Home Visitation on Government Spending." *Medical Care* 1993;31(2):155-174.

Olds DL, Eckenrode J, Henderson CR Jr, Kitzman H, Powers J, Cole R, et al. "Long-Term Effects of Home Visitation on Maternal Life Course and Child Abuse and Neglect." *Journal of the American Medical Association* 1997;278(8):37-43.

Olds DL, Henderson CR Jr, Cole R, Eckenrode J, Kitzman H, Luckey D, et al. "Long-Term Effects of Nurse Home Visitation on Children's Criminal and Antisocial Behavior: 15-Year Follow-Up of a Randomized Trial." *Journal of the American Medical Association* 1998;280(14):1238-1244.

Olds DL. "Home Visiting: Searching for Answers on Effectiveness." Zero to Three Home Visiting Summit at the National Training Institutes; 1998 Dec 5; Washington, DC.

Olds DL, Henderson CR Jr, Kitzman H, Eckenrode J, Cole R, Tatelbaum R. "Prenatal and Infancy Home Visitation by Nurses: Recent Findings." *Future of Children* 1999;9(1):44-65.

Powell DR. "Inside Home Visiting Programs." *Future of Children* 1993;3(3):23-38.

Rivara FP, Farrington DP. "Prevention of Violence: Role of the Pediatrician." *Archives of Pediatrics and Adolescent Medicine* 1995;149(4):421-429.

Slaughter-Defoe DT. "Home Visiting with Families in Poverty: Introducing the Concept of Culture." *Future of Children* 1993;3(3):172-183.

Wallach VA. "Home-Based Family Support Services: Part of the Comprehensive National Plan To Improve the Overall Health and Safety of Children." *Hawaii Medical Journal* 1994;53(9):252-253, 261.

Wasik BH, Roberts RH. "Survey of Home Visiting Programs for Abused and Neglected Children and Their Families." *Child Abuse and Neglect* 1994;18(3):7271-283.

Weiss HB. "Home Visits: Necessary But Not Sufficient." *Future of Children* 1993;3(3):113-128.

Widom CS. "The Cycle of Violence." National Institute of Justice: Research in Brief, October 1992. Cited in Feindler EL, Becker JV. "Interventions in Family Violence Involving Children and Adolescents." In: Eron LD, Gentry JH, Schlegel P, editors. *Reason To Hope: A Psychosocial Perspective on Violence and Youth.* Washington, DC: American Psychological Association, 1994: 405-430.

Wolfner GD, Gelles RJ. "A Profile of Violence Toward Children: A National Study." *Child Abuse and Neglect* 1993;17(2):197- 212.

ADDITIONAL RESOURCES ON
HOME-VISITING INTERVENTIONS

Publications

The following publications contain helpful information about home-visiting interventions.

Barnard KE. "Developing, Implementing, and Documenting Interventions with Parents and Young Children." ***Zero to Three*** **1998; 4(February/March):23-29.** Barnard discusses the three issues that intervention planners, administrators, researchers, and policy makers must address: the implementation gap (the capacity to implement the interventions as conceptualized), the relationships between participants and the intervention staff/therapists, and the need for more intervention focus with parents and young children.

Zero to Three: National Center for Infants, Toddlers and Families
734 15th St., NW
Washington, DC 20005
Phone: 202-638-1144
Web site: www.zerotothree.org

Cohen LR, Shaeffer LG, Gordon AN, Baird TL. *Child Development, Health, and Safety: Educational Materials for Home Visitors and Parents.* **Gaithersburg, MD: Aspen Publishers, 1996.** A compilation of educational materials for use by home visitors to help prevent unintentional injuries and child abuse and neglect. The focus on preventing abuse and neglect is implicit rather than explicit so parents will not feel as though they are being targeted as potential abusers.

The Future of Children **1993; 3(3).** *The Future of Children* **1999; 9(1).** Published by The David and Lucile Packard Foundation, both issues are dedicated to home-visiting interventions. Articles describe the status of home-visiting interventions, recommend how to expand or improve home-visiting interventions, describe the diversity among families served by home-visiting interventions, and discuss recommendations by the U.S. Advisory Board on Child Abuse and Neglect to implement a national program of universal home visiting as a strategy to prevent child abuse and neglect.

David and Lucile Packard Foundation
300 Second St., Suite 200
Los Altos, CA 94022
Phone: 650-948-7658
Web site: www.packfound.org

Hanks C, Kitzman H, Milligan R. "Implementing the COACH Relationship Model: Health Promotion for Mothers and Children." *Advances in Nursing Science* **1996; 19(2): 57-66.** The COACH Relationship Model was part of a clinical trial to study the effect of nurse home visitation in improving the health-related behaviors of low-income mothers. After being taught the program's theoretical underpinnings (caring, ecological, role supplementation, and self-efficacy theories), nurses developed program materials to translate the concepts into nursing interventions.

Health Care Coalition on Violence. *A Review of the Research on Home Visiting: A Strategy for Preventing Child Maltreatment.* **Anoka, Minnesota: Health Care Coalition on Violence, 1998.** A review of 42 home-visiting research articles that describe child maltreatment in the United States and Minnesota, summarize the current research on home visiting, and recommend a future research agenda for home-visiting services. The review concludes that home visiting is an effective strategy for reducing the incidence of and risk for child maltreatment, but it leaves unresolved the components necessary for an effective program and the costs and benefits compared with other interventions.

Health Care Coalition on Violence
2829 Verndale Ave.
Anoka, MN 55303-1593
Phone: 612-576-1825
Fax: 612-427-7841

Healthy Families America (HFA) Community Planning and Site Development Guide, **January 1997.** Includes general HFA information; how to determine community needs; starting and implementing an HFA program; training; and research, evaluation, and quality assurance. Appendices include policies, sample worksheets, and 10 site summaries.

Prevent Child Abuse America
(formerly the National Committee to Prevent Child Abuse)
200 South Michigan Ave., 17th Floor
Chicago, IL 60604-2404
Phone: 312-663-3520
Fax: 312-939-8962

Healthy Families Indiana. Strategic Plan (1996) and Evaluation of Training (10/93-9/95). Healthy Families Indiana is a home-visiting intervention that provides long-term benefits to Indiana's families and children through services that promote family functioning and parent-child interaction, improve family and child health, and enhance child development.

Family and Social Services Administration/DFC
402 West Washington St., Room W364
Indianapolis, IN 46204
Phone: 317-232-4770
Fax: 317-232-4436

Journal of Community Psychology **1997; 25(1).** *Journal of Community Psychology* **1998; 26(1).** These issues discuss home visiting exclusively.

MacMillan HL, MacMillan JH, Offord DR, Griffith L, MacMillan A. "Primary Prevention of Child Physical Abuse and Neglect: A Critical Review. Part I." *Journal of Child Psychology* **1994; 35(5):835-856.** This article reviews the effectiveness of prospective controlled trials, published between January 1979 and May 1993, aimed at the primary prevention of child physical abuse and neglect. Interventions were classified into six categories within the broad group of perinatal and early childhood programs. Many of these programs did not show a reduction in physical abuse or neglect; however, there is evidence that extended home visitation can prevent physical abuse and neglect among disadvantaged families.

Oregon State University Healthy Start Evaluation Project. *Oregon's Healthy Start Effort, 1996-97 Status Report,* **December 1997.** Includes history, goals, Healthy Start model, reaching first-birth families, family assessment, participation, family characteristics, engagement and retention, and family satisfaction.

Family Study Center
Oregon State University
203 Bates Hall
Corvallis, OR 97331-5151
Phone: 541-737-2035

Powers M. "An Ounce of Prevention: Prenatal Care and Postnatal Intervention for At-Risk Mothers." *Human Ecology Forum* **1995; 23(1):19-22.** This article describes a 5-year longitudinal study to determine the sustainability of promising effects revealed in earlier studies, including better pregnancy outcomes, improved child care practices, fewer cases of child abuse, less reliance on social services, and a better life for mothers.

Zero to Three, Home Visiting with Families with Infants and Toddlers **1997; 17(4).** The entire issue is about home visiting. Various authors discuss the benefits and dilemmas of home visiting as a strategy to support families with infants and toddlers. Topics include universal access, intensive outreach to at-risk families, and community development as the ultimate goals. The overarching theme is that home visiting is a powerful tool but it is only the beginning of the work at hand.

Zero to Three: National Center for
Infants, Toddlers and Families
734 15th St., NW
Washington, DC 20005
Phone: 202-638-1144
Web site: www.zerotothree.org

Home-Visiting Programs

You may wish to contact the programs listed below, which have home-visiting components.

First Steps/Fremont County Family Center

First Steps offers comprehensive child-development and parenting services for families with children from birth to 5 years. The intervention, which operates as part of the Fremont County Family Center, also provides monthly home visits. Play groups are held 4 times a week for children, siblings, and parents.

Katherine Bair, Homevisiting Coordinator
1401 Oak Creek Grade Rd.
Canon City, CO 81212
Phone: 719-269-1523
E-mail: fcfc@ris.net

Health Start Partnership and CARES Parenting Program

This intervention fosters secure mother-infant attachments by encouraging responsive parenting. For 2 years, cohorts of 8 to 12 women with infants participate in home visits and weekly support and education groups. The program also provides medical care, lunch, and transportation.

Gloria Ferguson, Team Leader
491 West University Ave.
St. Paul, MN 55103-1936
Phone: 612-221-4368
E-mail: gloria.j.ferguson@healthpartners.com

Healthy Families Indiana

This voluntary home-visitation intervention is designed to promote healthy families and children. The intervention serves at-risk families with children from birth to 5 years. The family support worker visits weekly and helps increase parenting skills, healthy pregnancy practices, and referral to community resources.

Phyllis Kikendall
Indiana Family and Social Services Administration
402 West Washington St., W384
Indianapolis, IN 46204
Phone: 317-232-4770

Prenatal and Early Childhood Nurse Home Visitation Program

In this intervention, visits by nurse home visitors improve the health and social functioning of low-income first-time mothers and their babies. The home visits begin in pregnancy and continue until the child is 2 years old. Visit protocols focus on personal health, environmental health, maternal role, maternal life course, and family and friend support.

Ruth A. O'Brien, Ph.D.
Kempe Prevention Research Center for Family and Child Health
1825 Marion St.
Denver, CO 80218
Phone: 303-864-5210
E-mail: obrien.ruth@tchden.org

Healthy Families America Research Network Participants

Alaska

Debra L. Caldera
State of Alaska
Section of Maternal, Child, and Family Health
1231 Gambell St.
Anchorage, AL 99501
Phone: 907-269-3403
Fax: 907-269-3432
E-mail: DLCALDER@health.state.ak.us

Arizona

John Ashford
Arizona State University

School of Social Work, Room 245
Tempe, AZ 85287-1802
Phone: 602-965-1307
Fax: 602-965-5986
E-mail: atjba@asuvm.inre.asu.edu

Elizabeth Holtzapple
Arizona Office of the Auditor General
2910 N. 44th St., Suite 410
Phoenix, AZ 85108
Phone: 602-553-0333 (ext. 130)
Fax: 602-553-0051

Craig LeCroy
LeCroy & Milligan Associates, Inc.
620 N. Country Club, Suite B
Tucson, AZ 85716
Phone: 520-326-5154 (ext. 15)
Fax: 520-326-5155
E-mail: clecroy@u.arizona.ed

California

Lynn Cannady
LPC Consulting Associates
P.O. Box 188529
Sacramento, CA 95818
Phone: 916-448-8026
Fax: 916-447-8780
E-mail: cannady@ford-consulting.com

Terry Carrilio, Director
San Diego State University
School of Social Work
Policy Institute
9245 Sky Park Court, Suite 228
San Diego, CA 92123
Phone: 619-594-8610
Fax: 619-594-8600
E-mail: tbear10009@aol.com

Jerome Evans
Coordinator, Program Evaluation
Landon Pediatric Foundation
124 Poli St.
Ventura, CA 93001-2643
Phone: 805-643-5604
Fax: 805-643-5517
E-mail: jrevansphd@aol.com

John Landsverk
Director of Research
Services Research Center
Children's Hospital-San Diego
3020 Children's Way, MC 5033
San Diego, CA 92123-4282
Phone: 619-495-7703 ext. 3755
Fax: 619-495-7704
E-mail: jlandsverk@aol.com

Connecticut

Tim Black, Director
Center for Social Research
Department of Sociology
University of Hartford
200 Bloomfield Ave.
West Hartford, CT 06117-1599
Phone: 860-768-4026
Fax: 860-768-4080
E-mail: TBlack@uhavax.hartford.edu

Jack Powell
Department of Psychology
University of Hartford
200 Bloomfield Ave.
West Hartford, CT 06117-1599
Phone: 860-768-4720
Fax: 860-768-5292
E-mail: JPOWELL@MAIL.HARTFORD.EDU

Mary Steir
Associate Professor
Department of Psychology
200 Bloomfield Ave.
University of Hartford
West Hartford, CT 06117-1599
Phone: 860-768-5104
Fax: 860-768-5292
E-mail: steir@uhavax.hartford.edu

Florida

Sharon Carnahan
Department of Psychology
Rollins College
1000 Holt Ave.-2760
Winter Park, FL 32789-4499
Phone: 407-646-1557
Fax: 407-646-2685
E-mail: carnahan@rollins.edu

Carnot Nelson
Department of Psychology
University of South Florida
4200 E. Fowler Ave., BEH 339
Tampa, FL 33620-8200
Phone: 813-974-0471
Fax: 813-974-4617
E-mail: cnelson@luna.cas.usf.edu

Dan Perkins
University of Florida
Department of Family, Youth, and Community Sciences
3041 McCarty Hall
P.O. Box 110310
Gainesville, FL 32611-0310
Phone: 352-392-2201
Fax: 352-392-8196
E-mail: dperkins@gnv.lfas.ufl.edu

Judith Williams
Williams, Stern & Associates
3050 Biscayne Blvd., Suite 307
Miami, FL 33137
Phone: 305-573-4002
Fax: 305-573-4007
e-mail: willstar@bellsouth.net

Georgia

Julie Chambliss
1013 Muirfield Dr.
Marietta, GA 30068
Phone: 770-579-2726
Fax: 770-579-0225
E-mail: jwchamblis@aol.com

Hawaii

Anne Duggan
School of Medicine
Johns Hopkins University
600 N. Wolfe, SL/CMSC
Baltimore, MD 21287-3144
Phone: 410-614-0911
Fax: 410-550-5440
E-mail: awindham@jhu.edu

Illinois

Mary Castanuela
Ounce of Prevention Fund
122 S. Michigan Ave., Suite 2050
Chicago, IL 60603
Phone: 312-922-3863
Fax: 312-922-3337

Joel Milner
Northern Illinois University
Psychology Department
DeKalb, IL 60115-2892
Phone: 815-753-0739
E-mail: jmilner@niu.edu

Michael Sullivan
Ounce of Prevention Fund
122 S. Michigan Ave., Suite 2050
Chicago, IL 60603
Phone: 312-922-3863
Fax: 312-922-3337

Indiana

Jim Elicker
Department of Child Development and Family Studies
Purdue University
1269 Fowler House
West Lafayette, IN 47907-1269
Phone: 765-494-2938
Fax: 765-494-0503
E-mail: ELICKERJ@cfs.purdue.edu

Judith Myers-Walls
Department of Child Development and Family Studies
Purdue University
1269 Fowler House
West Lafayette, IN 47907-1269
Phone: 765-494-2959
Fax: 765-494-0503
E-mail: myerswal@cfs.purdue.edu

Iowa

Perle Slavik-Cowen
Assistant Professor
University of Iowa
472 College of Nursing
Iowa City, IA 52242-1121
Phone: 319-335-7117
Fax: 319-335-9990
e-mail: perle-cowen@uiowa.edu

Kentucky

Betty Shiels
Family and Children's Counseling Centers
209 Executive Park

Louisville, KY 40207
Phone: 502-895-4671
Fax: 502-893-3251
E-mail: SPIRITPC@aol.com

Maine

Ann B. Keith
University of Southern Maine
Masterton Hall
P.O. Box 9300
Portland, ME 04104-9300
Phone: 207-780-4138
Fax: 207-780-4997
E-mail: akeith@usm.maine.edu

Massachusetts

Anne Brady
Healthy Families Evaluation Project
Eliot-Pearson Department of Child Development
Tufts University
105 College Ave.
Medford, MA 02155
Phone: 617-627-3866
Fax: 617-627-3503
E-mail: abrady@emerald.tufts.edu

M. Ann Easterbrooks
Healthy Families Evaluation Project
Eliot-Pearson Department of Child Development
Tufts University
105 College Ave.
Medford, MA 02155
Phone: 617-627-5000 (ext. 2217)
Fax: 617-627-3503
E-mail: aeasterb@emerald.tufts.edu

Fran Jacobs
Healthy Families Evaluation Project
Eliot-Pearson Department of Child Development
Tufts University

105 College Ave.
Medford, MA 02155
Phone: 617-627-3355
Fax: 617-627-3503

Michigan

Cynthia Schellenbach
Department of Psychology
Oakland University
119 Pryale Hall
Rochester, MI 48309
Phone: 248-370-2310
Fax: 248-370-4612
E-mail: schellen@oakland.edu

Minnesota

Richard Chase
Wilder Foundation
Wilder Research Center
1295 Bandana Blvd. North, #210
St. Paul, MN 55108
Phone: 612-647-4517
Fax: 612-647-4623
E-mail: rick@wilder.org

LaVohn Josten
School of Nursing
University of Minnesota
308 Harvard St., SE
Minneapolis, MN 55455
Phone: 612-624-5139
Fax: 612-626-2359
E-mail: Joste001@UMN.TC.edu

Barbara Palmer
Minnesota Healthy Beginnings
Minnesota Department of Health
717 SE Delaware St.
P.O. Box 9441
Minneapolis, MN 55455

Phone: 651-281-9864
Fax: 651-215-8959
E-mail: barb.palmer@health.state.ms.us

Montana

Mary Trankel
Trankel Research and Analysis
P.O. Box 4153
Misscula, MT 59806-4153
Phone: 406-721-3803
Fax: 406-543-3803
E-mail: trankel@marsweb.com

Nevada

Sally Martin
University of Nevada-Reno
Human Development and Family Studies
Mailstop 140
Reno, NV 89557
Phone: 702-784-6490
Fax: 702-784-6493
E-mail: smartin@scs.unr.edu

New Jersey

Carla Woodson
Prevent Child Abuse-New Jersey
103 Church St., Suite 210
New Brunswick, NJ 08901
Phone: 732-246-8060
Fax: 732-246-1776
E-mail: preventchildabuse@worldnet.att.net

New York

Elizabeth Anisfeld
Best Beginnings
2410 Amsterdam Ave., 2nd Floor
New York, NY 10033
Phone: 212-923-5440
Fax: 212-923-5509
E-mail: ea6@columbia.edu

Rose Greene
Center for Human Services Research and Evaluation
Rockefeller College
University of Albany
301 Richardson Hall
135 Western Ave.
Albany, NY 12222
Phone: 518-442-5774
Fax: 518-442-5768
E-mail: rgreene@cnsvax.albany.edu

Nell B. Guterman
Columbia University
School of Social Work
622 W. 113th St.
New York, NY 10025
Phone: 212-854-5371
Fax: 212-854-2975
E-mail: nbg2@columbia.edu

John Heck
Professional Development Program
Rockefeller University
University of Albany
301 Richardson Hall
135 Western Ave.
Albany, NY 12222
Phone: 518-442-5719
Fax: 518-442-5719
E-mail: jheck@pdp.albany.edu

Susan Mitchell-Herzfeld
New York State Department of Social Services
Office of Program Evaluation
40 N. Pearl St., 14C
Albany, NY 12243
Phone: 518-474-9486
Fax: 518-473-8205
E-mail: 0pe0502@dfa.state.ny.us

Virginia Rauh
1129 Rock Creek Rd.
Gladwyne, PA 19035
Phone: 610-896-6868
Fax: 610-896-9499
E-mail: RAUHV@wpd.auhs.edu

Ohio

David Corwin
The Childhood Trust, ML0539
Department of Psychology
Logan Hall Roof
3259 Elland Ave.
Cincinnati, OH 45267-0539
Phone: 513-558-4067
E-mail: david.corwin@uc.edu

Jennifer Sharma
Beech Acres
Administrative Office
6881 Beechmont Ave.
Cincinnati, OH 45230-2093
Phone: 513-751-0400
Fax: 513-751-0403
E-mail: jsharma@beechacres.org

Oklahoma

Anne McDonald Culp
University of Alabama
Human Development and Family Studies
Box 870158
Tuscaloosa, AL 35487-0158
Phone: 205-348-6172
Fax: 205-348-3789
E-mail: aculp@okway.okstate.edu

Oregon

Aphra Katzev
Family Study Center, Bates 203
Oregon State University

Corvallis, OR 97331-5151
Phone: 541-737-2035
Fax: 541-737-5579
E-mail: katzeva@ucs.orst.edu

Clara Pratt
Family Study Center, Bates 204
Oregon State University
Corvallis, OR 97331-5151
Phone: 541-737-1084
Fax: 541-737-5579
E-mail: prattc@ccmail.orst.edu

South Carolina

Elisabeth Brown
1185 Lakehurst Dr.
Rock Hill, SC 29732
Phone: 803-328-0815
E-mail: elsbethb@juno.com

Tennessee

Barbara Clinton
MIHOW
Center for Health Services
Vanderbilt University
Station 17, Box 567
Nashville, TN 37232-8180
Phone: 615-322-4176
Fax: 615-343-0325
E-mail: barbara.m.clinton@vanderbilt.edu

Bingham G. Pope
University of Tennessee
School of Social Work
Office of Research and Public Services
Henson Hall, Room 319
1618 Cumberland Ave.
Knoxville, TN 37996-3334
Phone: 423-974-6015
Fax: 423-974-3877

E-mail: bgpope@utk.edu

Texas

Dr. Hope Nora
Healthy Family Initiatives
7500 Beechnut, Suite 227
Houston, TX 77074
Phone: 713-270-8849
Fax: 713-270-9532

Elizabeth Jones
Texas Department of Human Planning, Evaluating,
and Project Management
Mail Code W616
701 W. 51st St.
Austin, TX 76714-9030
Phone: 512-438-2479
Fax: 512-451-8199
E-mail: elizabeth.jones@dhs.state.tx.us

Utah

Glenna Boyce
Early Intervention Research Initiative
Utah State University
Logan, UT 84322-6580
Phone: 435-797-1179
Fax: 435-797-2019
E-mail: Glenna@CPD2.usu.edu

Richard Roberts
Early Intervention Research Institute
Utah State University
Logan, UT 84322-6580
Phone: 435-797-3346
Fax: 435-797-2019
E-mail: RICHR@CPD2.usu.edu

Vermont

Moshe Braner
Vermont Department of Health

Health Surveillance
108 Cherry St.
Burlington, VT 05402
Phone: 802-865-7703
Fax: 802-865-7701
E-mail: mbraner@vdh.state.vt.us

Virginia

Barbara Barrett
6 Wallace Farms Lane
Fredericksburg, VA 22406-5136
Phone: 540-372-3460
Fax: 540-372-3706
E-mail: 71077.2664@compuserve.com

Joseph Galano
Department of Psychology
College of William and Mary
Williamsburg, VA 23187-8795
Phone: 757-221-3878
Fax: 757-221-3896
E-mail: jxgala@facstaff.wm.edu

Lee Huntington
Huntington Associates
2300 Providence Creek Rd.
Richmond, VA 23236
Phone: 804-276-9015
Fax: 804-276-9016
E-mail: lhuntington@erols.com

Darcy Strouse
Aspen Systems Corporation
2277 Research Blvd., Mailstop 9T
Rockville, MD 20850
Phone: 301-519-5284
Fax: 301-519-6616
E-mail: dstrouse@aspensys.com

Wisconsin
Ann Kelm
Family Living Education
Cooperative Extension Service
University of Wisconsin-Madison
434 Lowell Hall
610 Langdon St.
Madison, WI 53706
Phone: 608-262-2453
Fax: 608-263-7969
E-mail: akelm@facstaff.wisc.edu

SOCIAL COGNITIVE-STRATEGY

Social-cognitive interventions strive to equip children with the skills they need to deal effectively with difficult social situations.

Overview of the Social-Cognitive Strategy

Researchers have linked a lack of social problem-solving skills to youth violence (Pepler and Slaby 1994; Baranowski et al. 1997). When children and adolescents are faced with social situations for which they are unprepared emotionally and cognitively, they may respond with aggression or violence. Many assert that we can improve children's ability to avoid violent situations and solve problems nonviolently by enhancing their social relationships with peers, teaching them how to interpret behavioral cues, and improving their conflict-resolution skills (Nadel et al. 1996).

Social-cognitive interventions strive to equip children with the skills they need to deal effectively with difficult social situations, such as being teased or being the last one picked to join a team. They build on Bandura's social-cognitive theory, which posits that children learn social skills by observing and interacting with parents, adult relatives and friends, teachers, peers, and others in the environment, including media role models (Bandura 1986). Social-cognitive interventions incorporate didactic teaching, modeling, and role-playing to enhance positive social interactions, teach nonviolent methods for resolving conflict, and establish or strengthen nonviolent beliefs in young people.

Best Practices for a Social-Cognitive Intervention

While evaluations have shown social-cognitive interventions to be effective in the short-term, long-term effectiveness is still unclear. However, even with limited data, we can offer best practices for developing and implementing this type of intervention. The recommendations that follow are based on an extensive literature review and on interviews and surveys conducted with experts in the field of youth violence prevention.

Identify the Populations You Want to Reach

Social-cognitive interventions are typically aimed at children. The younger participants are when your effort begins, the better your chances of successfully preventing aggressive attitudes and behaviors (Slaby 1998). Ideally, these interventions should reach all young people in a community, not just those with a history of violent behavior. However, if your community is like most, limited resources may prohibit such a large-scale effort. To determine who your intended participants should be, assess the community's needs and the money, time, and human resources available.

If you choose to target both violent and nonviolent children, use caution in planning your intervention activities. While violent children may be positively influenced by nonviolent participants, children with high levels of aggression need special attention. They may not thrive in an intervention intended for a general population. And if the ratio of violent to nonviolent children is too high, the nonviolent children could be negatively influenced.

Consider the Cultural and Demographic Context of Intended Participants

Social-cognitive interventions must take into account the environment in which participants live and the circumstances they face. Children who exhibit violent behaviors often come from neighborhoods in which risk factors such as poverty, drug or alcohol abuse, and divorce are commonplace. Interventions must address these issues, in addition to teaching social and conflict-resolution skills. They must also be sensitive to the views of individual schools, the school system's administrators, and the community as a whole.

Select an Appropriate Setting

Most social-cognitive interventions reported in the literature are centered in the schools for practical reasons. Trainers are often already on site, and children gather there for seven to eight hours a day, five days a week. Also, schools can set policies and alter the physical surroundings to minimize risk factors for violence, thus creating a model environment.

The younger participants are when your effort begins, the better your chances of successfully preventing aggressive attitudes and behaviors.

However, social-cognitive interventions need not be limited to school settings; they can be conducted wherever children are found in organized groups. Because patterns of violence appear to develop at an early age, researchers suggest that violence prevention efforts begin when children are very young and continue throughout their school years (Kellam et al. 1994; Slaby 1998). Therefore, social-cognitive interventions may ideally be introduced in Head Start programs, preschools, and childcare centers.

Additionally, efforts should be made to reach children who have dropped out of school. This may mean developing interventions to be carried out in community centers, churches, and juvenile detention facilities.

Involve the Community

Social-cognitive interventions cannot succeed in a vacuum. The surrounding community must be engaged in violence prevention activities that support the school-based effort. In addition, parents and caregivers must reinforce the learning that goes on inside the classroom.

The School Community

The effectiveness of social-cognitive interventions depends largely on a whole-school approach (Aber et al. 1996; Wiist, Jackson, and Jackson 1996; Orpinas et al. 1996). In other words, all members of the school community—from administrators to teachers to students and other school personnel—should have a role.

To achieve such an integrated system, intervention planners should establish a steering committee or core group within the school or school district to coordinate activities. This group should work closely with school principals and other administrators to ensure that the intervention's activities are in line with the school's or district's goals and to increase the commitment level of decision makers (Aber et al. 1996; Wiist, Jackson, and Jackson 1996; Orpinas et al. 1996). Supervisors should also be encouraged to support the professional development and training that teachers and other educators need to effectively implement the intervention and to allow intervention staff extra time to meet project deadlines.

Parents and Others

No matter how intensive and well-conceived school-based interventions are, they will probably not be successful without the approval, cooperation, and support of parents and the community (Powell, Muir-McClain, and Halasyamani 1995). Practitioners planning a social-cognitive intervention should recruit one or more credible, respected individuals in the school to promote the intervention and find ways for parents, community leaders, and others to participate in developing the intervention's activities and curriculum.

Set Clear Goals and Objectives for Intervention Outcomes and Implementation

Social-cognitive interventions promote social competence by building communication skills and facilitating peer relationships. Their general goal is to improve young people's ability to avoid conflict and handle in nonviolent ways any conflict that does arise. Common objectives of social-cognitive interventions include reducing the number of children suspended for violent acts, reducing the number of students referred to school counselors for aggressive behavior, and increasing positive attitudes toward nonviolence. Of course, goals and objectives for individual schools or communities will vary depending on needs and resources.

Select the Best Intervention for Your Participants and Develop Appropriate Materials

The intervention selected for a given school or school system— and the activities and curriculum that comprise it—will depend largely on participants' ages and whether the goal is to change the behaviors and attitudes of all students or those of aggressive or violent students only. However, all social-cognitive interventions typically address the beliefs and attitudes that support aggressive behavior and teach the following skills (Greene 1998):

- negotiation, critical thinking, and decision making
- identifying, managing, and coping with feelings, including anger
- anticipating the consequences of one's aggressive verbal and nonverbal behavior
- finding nonviolent alternatives to conflict
- moral reasoning

Social-cognitive interventions promote social competence by building communication skills and facilitating peer relationships. Between ages 6 and 12, children's beliefs about aggression and their tendencies to attribute hostile intent to others' actions are developing rapidly.

When developing the curriculum and activities for your intervention, review interventions that have been tried in other schools. Assess whether the practices that made the intervention effective are applicable to your school or community. You may need to customize some components of the intervention, but do so cautiously. Changing significant elements can alter the intervention's effectiveness.

Experts in the field of youth violence prevention have identified the following additional suggestions for developing social-cognitive intervention materials (Aber et al. 1996; Wiist, Jackson, and Jackson 1996; Orpinas et al. 1996; Huesmann, Pierce, and Briggs 1996; Greene 1998):

- Involve teachers and principals from the beginning.

- Use the words children use with their peers when they are angry.
- Include role-playing and small-group exercises to help children practice pro-social, nonviolent behaviors and develop automatic positive responses.
- Include training in intercultural understanding so young people can tolerate differences and see others' points of view.
- Teach students about the risk factors or triggers that can lead to violent confrontation.

For the General Student Population

If a school or community wants to prevent aggressive behavior before it starts or wants to improve the overall attitude toward violence, a social-cognitive intervention that's aimed at all students is one possible strategy. This section describes interventions designed for the general student population.

Elementary School

Research has shown that between ages 6 and 12, children's beliefs about aggression and their tendencies to attribute hostile intent to others' actions are developing rapidly (Aber et al. 1996). Therefore, several interventions have been developed to target this age group.

The Resolving Conflict Creatively Program (RCCP) is designed to help elementary-school teachers and students learn nonviolent ways of resolving conflicts, prevent involvement with violent situations, and promote intercultural understanding. It has several components, including the following:

- Teachers are trained to incorporate into a traditional curriculum exercises to improve communication, conflict resolution, and inter-group relations.
- Staff developers guide teachers in applying new skills.
- Administrators are briefed about the intervention's concepts and how they can support the effort.
- Peer models for nonviolent conflict resolution intervene in arguments and disputes on the playground and in the lunchroom.

The RCCP curriculum contains 51 weekly lessons, each lasting 30 to 60 minutes. These lessons or "workshops" focus on active listening, assertiveness, emotional expression, perspective-taking, cooperation, negotiation, problem solving, conflict analysis, and countering expressions of bias. Teachers facilitate role-playing exercises, interviewing, small-group discussion, and brainstorming to achieve a high level of student interaction (Aber et al. 1996).

Evaluation of RCCP has revealed mixed results. The beliefs and thought processes that put students at risk for aggression increased among all students as the school-year progressed. However, when teachers administered many RCCP lessons, students' aggressive attitudes increased much more slowly. When teachers taught only a few RCCP lessons, students experienced a faster increase than average. In addition to the number of lessons taught, the context of the child's life was found to impact the effect of this program. The positive effects resulting from frequent exposure to the RCCP curriculum were weakened among children from high-risk classrooms and neighborhoods (Aber et al. 1998; Roderick 1998).

Peace-Builders is a school-wide intervention that teaches five principles: praise people, avoid put-downs, seek wise people as advisors and friends, notice and correct hurts we cause, and right wrongs. The program uses nine broad techniques for behavior change (Embry et al. 1996):

- common language for "community norms"
- real-life models and story characters who depict positive behaviors
- environmental cues to indicate desired behaviors
- role plays to increase the range of responses to conflict
- rehearsals of positive responses to negative situations
- rewards—both individual and group—for pro-social behaviors
- reduction in threats to reduce reactivity
- self- and peer monitoring
- activities to promote maintenance of change across time and context

Initial outcomes over a two-year period showed that exposure to Peace-Builders significantly increased teacher-rated social competence and student-reported pro-social behavior. Fewer effects were seen for students' aggressive behavior (Flannery et al., unpublished). Additionally, in a separate study assessing whether the program had any impact on visits to the school nurse, the researchers found that nurse visits—including those related to injuries—decreased 12 percent in intervention schools, while they remained static in comparison schools. The rates of injuries related to fighting showed little change in intervention schools, but they increased 56 percent in the comparison schools (Krug et al. 1997).

The PATHS (Promoting Alternative Thinking Strategies) Curriculum was developed to help students in kindergarten through fifth grade develop essential skills in emotional literacy, positive peer relations, and problem solving. Teachers blended intervention materials with the regular curriculum, and activities were conducted both in and out of the classroom. Parents were also given materials for use at home to help students generalize the lessons learned in class.

Four clinical trials of PATHS over the past 15 years have demonstrated improvements in social and emotional competencies and reductions in aggression and other risk factors (e.g., depression) across a wide range of elementary school children, including students with special needs. Some improvements were also seen in cognitive skills. These findings were reflected in teacher ratings, student self-reports, child testing and interviewing, and independent ratings by classroom observers (Greenberg et al. 1995; Greenberg and Kusche 1998). Second Step: A Violence Prevention Curriculum was developed to reduce aggression and increase pro-social behavior. Grossman and colleagues (1997) conducted a randomized trial among 790 second- and third-grade students in six matched pairs of urban and suburban elementary schools in Washington state. At both two weeks and six months after the intervention, the researchers found a moderate decrease in physical aggression and an increase in neutral and pro-social behavior in school. There was no measurement of behavior change outside the school setting. While this intervention appears promising for elementary schools, it has had disappointing effects when implemented in middle schools. In one study, the curriculum led to a decrease in boys' aggressive behaviors, but the results were short-lived (Orpinas et al. 1995). In a second study, the curriculum failed to reduce aggressive behaviors (Orpinas et al. 2000).

Middle School

Conflict Resolution: A Curriculum for Youth Providers is an intervention for middle-school students. Teachers present five chapters designed to build skills in communication and nonviolent conflict resolution. Students in classes that followed the curriculum reported significantly fewer violent solutions to hypothetical conflict situations than did students in other classes. The intervention group also reported significant decreases in the actual use of violence. Although the short-term results appear promising, the study used a quasi-experimental design to evaluate the curricula, and the students were not randomly selected. Therefore, interpretations of the results are limited (DuRant et al. 1996).

High School

The Violence Prevention Project (VPP), which was implemented in three high schools in Boston, involved students in lectures, discussions, and interactive role plays once a week for 10 weeks. Evaluation of the project found that very low suspension rates were maintained among juniors, but these rates were not always significantly different from groups who did not participate in the project. However, in a specialized class with a smaller student-teacher ratio and several services that were not available in the main school system, the project reduced suspension rates by 71 percent. Findings from this project suggest that the VPP can reduce negative school behaviors when other supportive activities and services are provided concurrently (Hausman, Pierce, and Briggs 1996).

For At-Risk and High-Risk Youth

Aggressive youths tend to have trouble with impulse control, problem solving, anger management, assertiveness, and empathy. Social-cognitive interventions are designed to improve interpersonal and problem-solving skills so these children will be less likely to resort to aggression or to become the target of violence and better able to negotiate mutually beneficial solutions (Slaby et al. 1995). High-risk youth should participate in interventions that use multiple components—for instance, academic enhancement and relationship building with both peers and adults. A broad, intensive intervention is needed to prevent violence by children with chronic aggressive behavior (Orpinas et al. 1996; Lochman et al. 1993).

Elementary School

The Brain-Power program is an attributional intervention designed to reduce peer-directed aggression among African American and Latino boys. During 60-minute sessions conducted twice weekly for six weeks, students engage in activities designed to reduce their tendencies to attribute hostile intentions in peers following ambiguous negative social interactions (Hudley 1994). A study of the Brain-Power intervention was conducted among 384 third- through sixth-grade students in four southern-California elementary schools.

> *A broad, intensive intervention is needed to prevent violence by children with chronic aggressive behavior.*

The students' behaviors and attitudes were measured for 12 months after the intervention. Boys in the intervention group improved their self-control and made fewer judgments of hostile intent. Although these results diminished over time, the findings suggest that improvements in behavior are related to changes in students' attributions (Hudley et al. 1998).

The Anger Coping Program and the Coping Power Program are related interventions designed for aggressive children who have a hard time accurately interpreting the intentions of others. Both interventions focus on developing children's abilities to manage anger, reducing their tendency to attribute hostile intent, and improving social problem-solving skills. The Anger Coping Program consists of 18 group sessions that are typically delivered in elementary schools. At three-year follow-up, the program had produced significant reductions in children's aggression in several pretest/post-test studies (Lochman, Burch, et al. 1984; Lochman, Lampron, et al. 1989) and reductions in substance use, but not in delinquency (Lochman 1992). The Coping Power Program has a 33-session child-group component and a 16-session parent-group component (Lochman and Welles 1996). Post-intervention and one-year follow-up evaluations showed significant reductions in children's aggression (Lochman, in press).

Middle School

Positive Adolescent Choices Training (PACT), implemented in Dayton, Ohio, was designed to reach high-risk African American students in seventh and eighth grades. The intervention's principle components include the following (Yung and Hammond 1995, 1998):

- Social-skills training—expressing anger, frustration, and disappointment constructively; listening and reacting appropriately to criticism or anger of others; and resolving disagreements nonviolently.
- Anger-management training—recognizing anger triggers, understanding anger responses, thinking through the consequences of those responses, and using techniques to control anger.
- Education about violence—dispelling myths about violence risks and raising awareness of the dynamics of violence.

Researchers found that youths in the PACT group expressed less physical aggression at school than did students in the control group. This improvement in behavior was observed both during and after the training. They also found that, compared to controls, PACT participants had less involvement with the juvenile court system, fewer violence-related charges, and lower rates of offenses per person (Yung and Hammond 1993).

Responding in Peaceful and Positive Ways (RIPP) is a sixth-grade curriculum that was taught in the Richmond Youth Against Violence Project. It was designed for students with high rates of suspension, low grade-point averages, absenteeism problems, and a history of violent behavior. About 90 percent of the students in the intervention were African American, and many came from low-income, single-parent households in neighborhoods with high rates of crime and drug use. The curriculum—developed from an earlier program based on Prothrow-Stith's model (1987) and the Children's Creative Response to Conflict Program (1988)—included 25 50-minute sessions implemented by specialists trained in conflict resolution (Farrell and Meyer 1997). All sessions combined behavioral repetition and mental rehearsal, experiential learning activities, and didactic learning opportunities. Early sessions focused on team building and expanding students' knowledge about nonviolence; later sessions focused on skill building and critical analysis. The skills taught in the sixth grade were reinforced by a school-wide peer-mediation intervention and by seventh- and eighth-grade curricula implemented by teachers (Meyer and Farrell 1998).

Results immediately following the intervention revealed that RIPP participants had significantly fewer disciplinary code violations, carried weapons less often, and were suspended less frequently than controls. Participants also improved their knowledge of intervention material, used their school's mediation program more frequently, and reported fewer injuries from fighting.

In a six-month follow-up study of RIPP, self-report data collected from 169 participants and 184 controls showed significant treatment effects for the frequency of violent behaviors, suppression of aggressive behavior, and knowledge of the intervention material. Impulse control improved significantly among boys, and fewer male students skipped school because of safety concerns. Significant improvement was seen in girls' reported use of nonviolent methods to address hypothetical conflict situations. School disciplinary data from the first semester of the seventh grade showed that RIPP participants had significantly fewer suspensions than the control group (Farrell, Meyer, and White 1998).

The Washington Community Violence Prevention Program offered fifth and seventh graders in high-crime areas of Washington, D.C., a curriculum to highlight the motivation behind aggressive behavior and develop problem-solving skills. The curriculum built on "Viewpoints," a 10-session intervention for violent juvenile offenders to which three sessions were added: one each on drugs and guns, and one to celebrate completion of the intervention (Guerra and Slaby 1990). Students increased their knowledge about risk factors for violence, changed their attitudes toward violence, and increased social skills shown to affect aggressive behavior. These effects were measured only in the short term (Gainer, Webster, and Champion 1993).

Aggressors, Victims, and Bystanders: Thinking and Acting to Prevent Violence is a curricular intervention for middle school students that focuses not only on aggressors, but also on the interrelated roles of victims and bystanders. It is based on the premise that all three players can build the cognitive and social skills needed to resolve problems nonviolently. The curriculum was developed and evaluated in three steps, each involving collaboration among expert advisors, teachers, and students. First, researchers assessed students' cognitive skills, beliefs, and tendency to start a conflict, be a victim, or be a bystander who encourages aggression. Second, a preliminary curriculum was developed, and teachers and students provided feedback on factors such as clarity, relevance, age appropriateness, engagement, and practical utility. Third, the curriculum was evaluated in a study of over 300 high-risk adolescents and a control group. The intervention reduced students' belief that violence is a favorable response to conflict; increased their intent to resolve conflict without aggression, seek relevant information, and avoid conflict; and improved their self-rated behavior, indicating withdrawal of bystander acceptance and encouragement of aggression (Slaby 1998).

Multi-Tier Interventions

Interventions designed for the general student population may fail to impact children at high risk for aggression. To address the needs of both the general and high-risk student populations, some practitioners plan interventions with several levels of activities. These multi-tier efforts may combine, for example, a curriculum to be delivered to all students with special small-group activities designed for high-risk youth. Some of these interventions also include activities for parents or the entire family.

One example of a multi-tier effort is the Metropolitan Area Child Study (MACS), an eight-year research trial conducted among elementary school students in urban, at-risk communities. Its goal was to change the thought processes and attitudes that are associated with aggressive behavior and to modify the school environment to foster pro-social development. Three components comprised MACS: a general enhancement classroom intervention, the "Yes I Can" curriculum; a small-group intervention for high-risk children; and a family component for the parents or guardians of high-risk children.

The "Yes I Can" curriculum consisted of 40 lessons delivered twice a week for two years (20 per year) by teachers in first-through sixth-grade classrooms. In the first year, students were taught self-understanding, relationship of self to others, and moral beliefs in order to motivate students to behave in pro-social ways and decrease their acceptance of aggression in social interactions. Also in the first year, teachers received 30 hours of training to help them model pro-social behaviors in the classroom. Year two introduced the themes of control and pro-social action plans to provide children with the skills needed for daily social interactions. The second year included monthly reviews for teachers to address the issues raised during first-year training and to help them develop plans for dealing with everyday classroom concerns.

The second component of MACS was a more intensive program directed at high-risk students. In addition to following the general enhancement curriculum, high-risk students participated in small-group activities designed to change their aggressive beliefs and attributions and give them opportunities to practice positive reactions to a variety of social situations. The small groups met once a week for 12 weeks in the first year and for 16 weeks in the second year. To increase social interaction, small-group participants were designated as leaders for the "Yes I Can" curriculum in the second year. Labeling the small-group activities as "leadership training meetings" helped motivate the high-risk students and improved their social status with peers. The third component of MACS was family-relationship training. This 22-week program was designed to address several factors related to children's antisocial behavior, including inconsistent discipline, low levels of parental monitoring, poor problem-solving skills, defensiveness in family interactions, and a lack of emotional bonding (Huesmann et al. 1996).

Multi-tier efforts may combine, for example, a curriculum to be delivered to all students with special small-group activities designed for high-risk youth. Incorporate an array of activities and materials in order to hold students' interest and model a variety of ways to prevent or counteract violence.

The results of this multi-level intervention were mixed. In schools with moderate resources, significant decreases in aggression were found among second- and third-grade students who received the most intensive intervention. However, in schools that had limited resources to devote to the intervention, aggression actually increased after the intervention, even when all three components were implemented. Among children in fifth and sixth grades, aggression increased after receiving general and small-group training, regardless of the school's resource level. These results indicate that a program like that tested in MACS can effectively decrease aggression if begun early and implemented in schools with adequate resources, but negative unintended effects may result when such an intervention is implemented among older students or in schools with limited means (Huesmann 2000).

Diverse Activities and Materials

Social-cognitive interventions should incorporate an array of activities and materials in order to hold students' interest and model a variety of ways to prevent or counteract violence. Multimedia formats, specifically computer-based interventions, can greatly enhance classroom instruction techniques because they provide flexibility and can spark interest among resistant students (Bosworth et al. 1996). The multimedia approach can adjust the intervention to students' responses, provide students control over the choice of information and sequence of materials, offer one-on-one anonymous interaction between the student and computer, and provide an attractive game-like atmosphere.

One multimedia example is SMART Team (formerly SMART Talk), a computer-based intervention for young adolescents that uses games, simulations, cartoons, animation, and interactive interviews to teach new ways of resolving conflict without violence. Computer characters act as role models who demonstrate anger management, dispute resolution, and perspective-taking to give adolescents strategies for conflict resolution and mediation (Bosworth et al. 1996). The intervention is composed of six modules that may be used in any order without losing continuity or impact. SMART Team was pilot tested with 102 seventh-grade students in a small-city middle school for a four-week period. The results showed significant increases in knowledge about conflict management and about behavior that escalates conflict; increases in self-reported pro-social behavior and intentions to use nonviolent strategies; and decreases in self-reported discipline problems at home, at school, and in the community. However, there was no difference in the students' confidence in handling conflict situations using nonviolent strategies (Bosworth, Espelage, and DuBay 1998).

The intervention was subsequently implemented in a large school in a major Midwestern metropolis with a diverse socioeconomic population. An evaluation of 516 sixth, seventh, and eighth graders showed that students found the intervention attractive and useful and that the intervention improved students' attitudes toward violence, increased self-awareness, and increased intentions to use nonviolent strategies. However, there were no significant changes in the frequency of aggressive behavior. The findings suggest that multimedia tools may be useful in changing some of the cognitive and psychological factors associated with violence and, therefore, have the potential for changing violent behavior (Bosworth et al. 2000).

Interventions to Address the School Setting and Social Norms

If interventions are to be effective in the school setting, issues about the setting itself must be addressed. Practitioners should include components that promote a nonviolent environment throughout the school. At a minimum, schools should have and enforce policies on safety precautions and student conduct. They should also enact non-punitive methods of control, encourage student involvement in academic and after-school activities, and provide continuous support for staff (Mayer 1995, 1999). A focus on the social context of the schools could help promote social competence and pro-social behavior in children by creating a caring school community (Baker 1998). School psychologists can help assess a school's culture and restructure schools to be more sensitive to social aspects of education, for example, by emphasizing personal responsibility, empathy, and respect for the community.

Addressing Violence in the Media

Violence is often glorified or romanticized in the news and entertainment media. This type of media coverage can give young people an unrealistic view of the consequences of violence and lead them to believe that violence is accepted— or even expected—in today's society. Social-cognitive interventions should teach media literacy to help children deconstruct the violent scenarios they see on television, watch in movies, and hear in song lyrics.

> *Social-cognitive interventions should help children deconstruct the violent scenarios they see on television, watch in movies, and hear in song lyrics.*

Cultural Considerations

Planners and practitioners should carefully review intervention materials and make necessary cultural adaptations for their intended participants.

Interventions reaching students living in transient neighborhoods, for example, must address the ethnic and language differences that are found in the community's heterogeneous population (Huesmann et al. 1996). It may be most effective to provide schools with a core curriculum to which they can add culturally appropriate material without compromising the intervention's effectiveness. Each school should research educational techniques that might work best for their students; no one technique is appropriate for all schools.

Link Social-Cognitive Interventions with Other Strategies

Interventions to prevent youth violence should involve multiple segments of children's social experiences and interactions. Studies have suggested that integrating the components of school-based social-cognitive interventions (e.g., social-skills development) with other types of interventions can improve effectiveness (Goldstein and McGinnis 1998; McGinnis and Goldstein 1998).

The FAST (Families and Schools Together) Track Program is a prime example of blending strategies to prevent youth violence. It combines a social-cognitive curriculum, parent training, and home visits to prevent conduct problems, promote social relations, and improve school performance among elementary school students. It has been implemented in the low-income, high-crime areas of Nashville, Tennessee; Seattle, Washington; Durham, North Carolina; and University Park, Pennsylvania (Bierman and Conduct 1996; Dodge and Conduct 1993). FAST Track is a multi-level program, consisting of universal and selective components. The universal component has a 57-lesson curriculum (the PATHS curriculum—see page 125) to foster universal development of emotional concepts, social understanding, and self-control. In the target communities, it was delivered to all students in 20- to 30-minute lessons, which were taught approximately three times a week (Catalano et al. 1998). Additional components were administered to high-risk students—

- Parents of high-risk children took part in training groups designed to promote positive family-school relationships and teach non-aggressive parenting skills (e.g., positive reinforcement, use of time outs, improved self-restraint).
- Home visits were conducted to foster parents' problem-solving skills, self-efficacy, and coping skills.
- High-risk students participated in social-skills training groups.
- Children received tutoring in reading.

- The at-risk children took part in a friendship-enhancement program called Peer Pairing.

The universal curriculum was applied each year for six years— from first through fifth grade—covering the important developmental transitions of school entry and moving from elementary to middle school. Home visits and tutoring took place weekly in the first-grade year; afterward, these activities occurred as dictated by participants' needs (Bierman and Conduct 1996).

At the completion of the first grade, children's social, emotional, and academic skills increased moderately; peer interactions and social status improved; and disruptive behaviors decreased. Parents reported decreased use of physical discipline, increased parenting satisfaction, and increased positive involvement with both their children and the school. Additionally, significant effects were seen in observer ratings of the classroom atmosphere, although assessment of classroom functioning varied by the quality of the FAST Track implementation (Conduct Problems Prevention Research Group 1999a, 1999b).

Coordinating Multi-Strategy Programs

When several strategies are incorporated into a program, you will likely need a diverse implementation staff. Persons best suited to carry out a school-based intervention, for example, may not be qualified to conduct home visits. Select one person or organization to coordinate hiring of staff, keep track of all activities in the various interventions, and monitor staff performance. This will ensure continuity among the interventions and improve the overall effort.

Select Staff Appropriate for Your Intervention

When staffing a social-cognitive intervention, there are basically three options: 1) teachers deliver the intervention in their classrooms; 2) full-time prevention specialists (who are not classroom teachers) implement the intervention; or 3) a combination of teachers and other professionals implement it. Each option has advantages and disadvantages, which are discussed below. But regardless of who implements your intervention, make sure staff members have a strong commitment to nonviolence and understand the social and environmental context of participants' lives.

Make sure staff members have a strong commitment to nonviolence.

Teachers as Implementers

Having teachers implement a social-cognitive intervention may increase the integration of intervention activities with the regular curriculum. And a teacher-based staff may require little or no additional funding. However, if teachers implement the intervention, students may be reluctant to disclose hostile or sensitive emotions. They may feel there is less confidentiality or fear that an admission of negative or aggressive feelings may result in lower grades or disciplinary action.

Be sure that teachers who participate in the intervention do so voluntarily (Aber et al. 1996; Wiist, Jackson, and Jackson 1996; Orpinas et al. 1996). Some teachers may resent the burden of adding extra activities to their already busy class schedule or be reluctant to spend extra time at school to carry out extracurricular intervention activities. These teachers may not devote the effort needed to make the intervention a success.

Limit intervention staff to those teachers who are enthusiastic about the activities and their intended results. In addition to being willing to devote extra effort to a social-cognitive intervention, teachers must believe that violence can be prevented and that the intervention they are implementing will have an impact (Slaby 1998). When teachers do not believe in violence prevention interventions but implement those interventions anyway, they may inadvertently weaken the intervention's effect or cause it to fail. You can assess individual teacher readiness by having teachers rate their beliefs about violence prevention efficacy at three levels:

- General beliefs—Do you believe that violence is preventable? If a teacher does not believe it is, he or she may misrepresent or ignore prevention messages.
- Specific beliefs—To what extent do you believe that prevention strategies and practices can be effective? If a teacher believes that violence is theoretically preventable but does not believe that intervention materials can be useful, he or she may not deliver activities and lessons effectively.
- Personal beliefs—Do you believe that you, personally, can make a difference in helping to prevent violence? A lack of personal efficacy can also limit effectiveness of intervention activities and messages.

You may need to increase readiness by providing evidence that these interventions work and that teachers can have a profound impact on youth violence prevention. For example, presenting a video or case study that shows skeptical teachers who implemented a violence prevention intervention and then noticed positive behavior changes may help convince staffers of their ability and that of the intervention to prevent violence (Slaby 1998).

Other Professionals as Implementers

In some cases, such as when after-school activities form a significant portion of an intervention, non-teachers may be the ideal implementers. Even when activities take place during school hours, you may opt to employ a staff specifically to implement your effort. This will reduce much of the burden on teachers.

Of course, one obvious disadvantage of hiring non-teacher staffers is the need for significant funding. Funding will be required for additional salaries or consulting fees. Additional funds may also be required to conduct interviews and background checks for these individuals. This funding may come from the schools themselves or from other sources, such as government grants or community organizations.

Both Teachers and Others as Implementers

Having both teachers and other professionals implement your intervention may allow you to reap the benefits and minimize the negative elements that both groups of implementers present. A combined staff can also increase the effectiveness of your intervention. A non-teacher staff can lead intervention activities, and teachers can add reinforcing elements to their regular curriculum.

Train Staff Members

Teachers and others who implement social-cognitive interventions require significant training. Schools and communities must be willing to devote the resources needed for this professional development. In addition to preparing staff members to carry out intervention activities, training should teach them how to do the following (Slaby et al. 1995):

> *Having both teachers and other professionals implement your intervention may allow you to reap the benefits and minimize the negative elements that both groups of implementers present.*

- Organize the school environment to minimize violence.
- Establish sound procedures to respond to violence in the classroom.

- Encourage children to learn nonviolent strategies from peers.
- Develop and implement a broad violence prevention plan for their schools and community.

Training Duration

Training should begin with at least three days of intensive course work and interactive exercises. But to be effective, training must be continued for as long as the intervention lasts. Ongoing training or consultation does not need to be on site. Follow-up can be through e-mail or videos, for instance. However, we should note that the effectiveness of different methods of follow-up training has not been determined.

Recruit Participants

When social-cognitive interventions are incorporated into regular curricula (e.g., a health education curriculum), recruitment is typically not necessary. Students can take part in the intervention simply by attending class regularly. However, if your intervention is targeted to high-risk students, you may need to recruit them to participate in special activities that take place outside of the classroom, such as small-group discussions, peer-leadership training, or after-school sessions.

Implement Your Intervention

The effectiveness of a social-cognitive intervention will depend on many implementation factors, including how often and for how long students are exposed to activities and messages, how well teachers and other intervention staffers are supported, and how interested students remain in the activities.

Match the Intervention's Frequency, Intensity, and Duration with Participants' Needs

If you are replicating an evaluated intervention, implement it as presented in the research in terms of frequency, intensity, and duration. When implementing a new intervention, the guidance that follows should help.

Students need frequent contact with intervention activities and materials. However, the actual number of contacts will depend on the material, the age or developmental readiness of participants, and the time needed to practice skills. Older students are better able to digest more information in one sitting. Elementary school students, because of their short attention spans, may need small "doses" of content. Social-cognitive interventions take a long time to effect changes.

A single curriculum with 10 to 15 sessions is likely to be insufficient (Orpinas 1995). Half a school year of violence prevention programming should be a minimum. For the longest-term impact, school districts should consider multi-year models with continuity across years. And for students who come into daily contact with violence outside the school setting, social-cognitive interventions should be a permanent part of school curricula (Slaby 1997).

Support Teachers and Other Intervention Staff

Social-cognitive interventions can be taxing for teachers and other staff. Facilitators should receive periodic training, receive feedback and encouragement from supervisors, and be thanked in a variety of ways. Incentives such as extra pay, continuing education units, and extra planning time may help keep intervention staff motivated.

Encourage Participants to Stay Involved

To keep students interested in the intervention, connect the activities to their goals. Show them how the behaviors they are learning will help them get what they want—improved safety at school and in their neighborhood, greater respect from peers, improved academic performance, and perhaps a larger circle of friends.

Make the intervention fun, and relate it to "real life." Include games and videotape the intervention activities to engage younger children. Use articles from local newspapers or magazines to start discussions about violence. Have students keep a log of violent images they see in the media and nonviolent examples of conflict resolution; use the log to generate class discussions. Ask young participants to share stories that illustrate nonviolent, pro-social behaviors. Let students know they will receive a tangible reward for completing the intervention. Students—and implementation staff—need a way to publicly acknowledge and celebrate their accomplishments (Aber et al. 1996; Wiist, Jackson, and Jackson 1996; Orpinas et al. 1996).

To keep students interested in the intervention, connect the activities to their goals.

Monitor Progress and the Quality of Implementation

Monitoring, which focuses on the process of implementation, is necessary to ensure that your intervention is on track. To determine if your social-cognitive intervention is reaching the intended population and being implemented as planned—

- Keep attendance records for intervention activities and record what happens during those activities.
- Observe classroom sessions periodically to see how intervention content is being delivered.
- Use staff meetings to obtain feedback from teachers and administrators about intervention delivery.

Review data routinely throughout implementation so you can correct any problems that might jeopardize the success of your effort.

Evaluate Outcomes

Evaluation allows you to assess the effectiveness of your intervention and identify any unexpected outcomes. For a social-cognitive intervention, you'll want to answer these questions:

- Did participants' knowledge about and attitudes toward violence change?
- Did aggressive and violent behaviors decrease?
- Were there any negative unintended effects from the intervention?

To obtain this data, review school records for attendance, truancy, and disciplinary actions. Keep in mind the school district's reporting requirements and the variability across schools in how offenses are reported and recorded. Collect teachers' perceptions of participants' behavior changes and ask students to report changes in their own and in peers' behaviors and attitudes. You can also hire someone who was not involved in the intervention to evaluate students' behaviors; this method may produce the most objective data.

Maintain Results after Implementation

Interventions to prevent youth violence are never finished. While positive changes are often seen right after an intervention ends, those improvements typically dissipate without reinforcement. Orpinas (1995) observed that self-reported aggressive behavior among students who participated in the Second Step program (discussed on page 125) increased as more time passed from the end of program implementation.

To maintain positive effects, practitioners should provide children and adolescents with reinforcing "booster" activities. Lochman (1992), for example, looked at the effects of a school-based anger-coping intervention several years after implementation. Although significant post-implementation results had been reported, there were no effects on delinquency rates or classroom behavior for most participants at the three-year follow-up. A subset of participants who received booster sessions did maintain positive behavior changes.

Planning and implementing booster activities requires support from teachers, administrators, students, and the community. To achieve this support, share evaluation results with teachers and other school staff so they'll know that they made a difference; involve intervention "alumni" in follow-up efforts; and establish collaborative relationships between the school and community organizations (e.g., health and wellness centers, youth centers, churches).

Summary

Social-cognitive interventions have been shown to reduce aggressive behavior by youth in the short term. Long-term evaluation, although it has been discussed for years (Coben et al. 1994), continues to be lacking. There are also several limitations to these interventions.

First, some of the more violent youths are not being reached by social-cognitive interventions because they do not attend traditional schools. Second, even with training, teachers and other implementers may vary in their delivery techniques; this variation can affect intervention outcomes. Third, participants may have difficulty translating the new behaviors they learn in school to the "real world." Finally, improvements in behaviors and attitudes that students and teachers report may not be accurate; awareness of desired outcomes may bias responses of both participants and implementers. Other measures, besides self- and teacher reports, must be developed to obtain more objective data.

To maintain positive effects, provide children and adolescents with reinforcing "booster" activities.

REFERENCES

Aber JL, Brown JL, Chaudry N, Jones SM, Samples F. "The Evaluation of the Resolving Conflict Creatively Program: An Overview." *American Journal of Preventive Medicine* 1996;12(5 Suppl):82-90.

Aber JL, Jones SM, Brown JL, Chaudry N, Samples F. "Resolving Conflict Creatively: Evaluating the Developmental Effects of a School-Based Violence Prevention Program in Neighborhood and Classroom Context." *Development and Psychopathology* 1998;10(2):187-213.

Baker JA. "Are We Missing the Forest for the Trees? Considering the Social Context of School Violence." *Journal of School Psychology* 1998;36(1):29-44.

Bandura A. *Social Foundations of Thought and Action: A Social Cognitive Theory.* Englewood Cliffs, NJ: Prentice-Hall, 1986.

Baranowski T, Perry CL, Parcel GS. "How Individuals, Environments, and Health Behavior Interact: Social Cognitive Theory." In: Glanz K, Lewis FM, Rimer BK, editors. *Health Behavior and Health Education: Theory, Research and Practice (2nd edition).* San Francisco: Jossey-Bass Publishers, 1997.

Bierman KL, Conduct Problems Prevention Research Group. "Integrating Social-Skills Training Interventions with Parent Training and Family-Focused Support to Prevent Conduct Disorders in High-Risk Populations: The FAST Track Multisite Demonstration Project." In: Ferris CF, Grisso T, editors. *Understanding Aggressive Behavior in Children. Annals of the New York Academy of Science, Vol. 794.* New York: New York Academy of Sciences, 1996: 256-264.

Bosworth K, Espelage D, DuBay T, Dahlberg LL, Daytner G. "Using Multimedia to Teach Conflict-Resolution Skills to Young Adolescents." *American Journal of Preventive Medicine* 1996;12(5 Suppl):65-74.

Bosworth K, Espelage D, DuBay T. "A Computer-Based Violence Prevention Intervention for Young Adolescents: Pilot Study." *Adolescence* 1998;33(132):785-795.

Bosworth K, Espelage D, DuBay T, Daytner G, Karageorge K. "Preliminary Evaluation of a Multimedia Violence Prevention Program for Adolescents." *American Journal of Health Behavior* 2000;24(4):268-280.

Catalano RF, Berglund ML, Ryan JAM, Lonczak HC, Hawkins JD. *Positive Youth Development in the United States: Research Findings on Evaluations of Positive Youth Development Programs.* Seattle: University of Washington School of Social Work, November 13, 1998.

(Funded by and submitted to the U.S. Department of Health and Human Services, Office of the Assistant Secretary for Planning and Evaluation, and the National Institute of Child Health and Human Development.)

Children's Creative Response to Conflict. *The Friendly Classroom for a Small Planet.* Philadelphia: New Society Publishers, 1988.

Coben JH, Weiss HB, Mulvey EP, Dearwater SR. "A Primer on School Violence Prevention." *Journal of School Health* 1994;64(8):309-313.

Conduct Problems Prevention Research Group. "Initial Impact of the FAST Track Prevention Trial for Conduct Problems I: The High-Risk Sample." *Journal of Consulting and Clinical Psychology* 1999;67(5):631-647.

Conduct Problems Prevention Research Group. "Initial Impact of the FAST Track Prevention Trial for Conduct Problems II: Classroom Effects." *Journal of Consulting and Clinical Psychology* 1999;67(5):648-657.

Dodge K, Conduct Problems Prevention Research Group. "Effects of Intervention on Children at High Risk for Conduct Problems." Paper presented at the biennial meeting of the Society for Research in Child Development; 1993 Mar; New Orleans (LA).

DuRant RH, Treiber F, Getts A, McCloud K, Linder CW, Woods ER. "Comparison of Two Violence Prevention Curricula for Middle School Adolescents." *Journal of Adolescent Health* 1996;19(2):111-117.

Embry DD, Flannery DJ, Vazsonyi AT, Powell KE, Atha H. "PeaceBuilders: A Theoretically Driven, School-based Model for Early Violence Prevention." *American Journal of Preventive Medicine* 1996;12(5 Suppl):91-100.

Farrell AD, Meyer AL, White KS. "Development and Evaluation of RIPP: A School-Based Violence Prevention Program for Urban Youth." In: Aber JL, chair. *Changing Trajectories to Youth Violence: Lessons Learned from Recent Intervention Studies.* Symposium presented at the biennial meeting of the Society for Research on Adolescence; 1998 Feb; San Diego (CA).

Farrell AD, Meyer AL. "The Effectiveness of a School-Based Curriculum for Reducing Violence among Urban Sixth-Grade Students." *American Journal of Public Health* 1997;87(6):979- 984.

Flannery DJ, Vazsonyi A, Embry D, Powell K, Atha H, Vesterdal W, et al. "Longitudinal Evidence of Effective School-Based Violence Prevention." Under review, May 2000. Gainer PS, Webster DW, Champion HR. "A Youth Violence Prevention Program." *Archives of Surgery* 1993;128(3):303-308.

Goldstein AP, McGinnis E. *Skillstreaming the Adolescent: New Strategies and Perspectives for Teaching Pro-social Skills.* Champaign, IL: Research Press, 1998: 218.

Greenberg MT, Kusche CA, Cook ET, Quamma JT. "Promoting Emotional Competence in School-Aged Children: The Effects of the PATHS Curriculum." *Development and Psychopathology* 1995;7(11):117-136.

Greenberg MT, Kusche CA. *Blueprints for Violence Prevention: Book Ten: Promoting Alternative Thinking Strategies.* Boulder, CO: Center for the Prevention of Violence, 1998.

Greene MB. "Youth Violence in the City: The Role of Educational Interventions." *Health Education and Behavior* 1998;25(2):175-193.

Grossman D, Neckerman HJ, Koepsell TD, Liu PY, Asher KN, Beland K, et al. "Effectiveness of a Violence Prevention Curriculum Among Children in Elementary School: A Randomized Controlled Trial." *Journal of the American Medical Association* 1997;277(20):1605-1611.

Guerra NG, Slaby RG. "Cognitive Mediators of Aggression in Adolescent Offenders: 2. Intervention." *Developmental Psychology* 1990;26(2):269-277.

Hausman A, Pierce G, Briggs L. "Evaluation of Comprehensive Violence Prevention Education: Effects on Student Behavior." *Journal of Adolescent Health* 1996;19(2):104-110.

Hudley CA. "The Reduction of Childhood Aggression Using the BrainPower Program." In: Furlong M, Smith D, editors. *Anger, Hostility, and Aggression: Assessment, Prevention, and Intervention Strategies for Youth.* Brandon, VT: Clinical Psychology Publishing Co., Inc., 1994.

Hudley CA, Britsch B, Wakefield WD, Smith T, Demorat M, Cho S. "An Attribution Retraining Program to Reduce Aggression in Elementary School Students." *Psychology in the Schools* 1998;35(3):271-282.

Huesmann LR, Maxwell CD, Eron L, Dahlberg LL, Guerra NG, Tolan PH, et al. "Evaluating a Cognitive/Ecological Program for the Prevention of Aggression Among Urban Children." *American Journal of Preventive Medicine* 1996;12(5 Suppl):120-128.

Huesmann LR. *An Evaluation of a Cognitive/Ecological Approach to the Prevention of Interpersonal Violence,* February 1, 2000. Final performance report for cooperative agreement U81/CCU510017-06, Evaluation of Specific Youth Violence Interventions, funded by the Centers for Disease Control and Prevention.

Kellam SG, Rebok GW, Ialongo N, Mayer LS. "The Course and Malleability of Aggressive Behavior from Early First Grade into Middle School: Results of a Developmental Epidemiologically Based

Preventive Trial." *Journal of Child Psychology and Psychiatry* 1994;35(2):259-281.

Krug EG, Brener ND, Dahlberg LL, Ryan GW, Powell KE. "The Impact of an Elementary School-Based Violence Prevention Program on Visits to the School Nurse." *American Journal of Preventive Medicine* 1997;13(6):459-463.

Lochman JE. "Cognitive-Behavioral Intervention with Aggressive Boys: Three-Year Follow-Up and Preventive Effects." *Journal of Consulting and Clinical Psychology* 1992;60(3):426-432.

Lochman JE. "Preventive Intervention with Precursors to Substance Abuse." In: Bukoski W, Sloboda Z, editors. *Handbook for Drug Abuse Prevention Theory, Science, and Practice.* New York: Plenum Publishers. In press, May 2000.

Lochman JE, Burch PR, Curry JF, Lampron LB. "Treatment and Generalization Effects of Cognitive-Behavioral and Goal-Setting Interventions with Aggressive Boys." *Journal of Consulting and Clinical Psychology* 1984;52(5):915-916.

Lochman JE, Dunn SE, Klimes-Dougan B. "An Intervention and Consultation Model from a Social Cognitive Perspective: A Description of the Anger Coping Program." *School Psychology Review* 1993;22(3):458-471.

Lochman JE, Lampron LB, Gemmer TC, Harris SR, Wyckoff GM. "Teacher Consultation and Cognitive-Behavioral Intervention with Aggressive Boys." *Psychology in the Schools* 1989;26(2):179-188.

Lochman JE, Welles KC. "A Social-Cognitive Intervention with Aggressive Children: Preventive Effects and Contextual Implementation. In: Peters RD, McMahon RJ, editors. *Prevention and Early Intervention: Childhood Disorders, Substance Use, and Delinquency.* Newbury Park, CA: Sage Publications, Inc., 1996: 111-143.

Mayer GR. "Preventing Antisocial Behavior in the School." *Journal of Applied Behavior Analysis* 1995;28(4):467-478.

Mayer GR. "Constructive Discipline for School Personnel." *Education and Treatment of Children* 1999;22(1):55-83.

McGinnis E, Goldstein AP. *Skillstreaming the Elementary School Child: New Strategies and Perspectives for Teaching Pro-social Skills, Revised Edition.* Champaign, IL: Research Press, 1998.

Meyer A, Farrell A. "Social Skills Training to Promote Resilience in Urban Sixth-Grade Students: One Product of an Action Research Strategy to Prevent Youth Violence in High- Risk Environments." *Education and Treatment of Children* 1998;21(4):461-488.

Nadel H, Spellmann M, Alvarez-Canino T, Lausell-Bryant LL, Landsberg G. "The Cycle of Violence and Victimization: A Study of the School-Based Intervention of a Multidisciplinary Youth Violence-Prevention Program." *American Journal of Preventive Medicine* 1996;12(5 Suppl):109-119.

Orpinas P, Parcel GS, McAlister A, Frankowski R. "Violence Prevention in Middle Schools: A Pilot Evaluation." *Journal of Adolescent Health* 1995;17(6):360-371.

Orpinas P, Kelder S, Murray N, Fourney A, Conroy J, McReynolds L, et al. "Critical Issues in Implementing a Comprehensive Violence Prevention Program for Middle Schools: Translating Theory Into Practice." *Education and Urban Society* 1996;28(4):456-472.

Orpinas P, Kelder S, Frankowski R, Murray N, Zhang Q, McAlister A. "Outcome Evaluation of a Multi-Component Violence Prevention Program for Middle Schools: The Students for Peace Project." *Health Education Research* 2000;15(1):45- 58.

Pepler D, Slaby RG. "Theoretical and Developmental Perspectives on Youth and Violence." In: Eron, LD, Gentry JH, Schlegel P, editors. *Reason to Hope: A Psychosocial Perspective on Violence and Youth.* Washington, DC: American Psychological Association, 1994: 27-58.

Powell KE, Muir-McClain L, Halasyamani L. "A Review of Selected School-Based Conflict Resolution and Peer Mediation Projects." *Journal of School Health* 1995;65(10):426-431.

Prothrow-Stith D. *Violence Prevention Curriculum for Adolescents.* Newton, MA: Education Development Center, Inc., 1987.

Roderick T. "Evaluating the Resolving Conflict Creatively Program." *The Fourth R* 1998;82:3-4.

Slaby RG. "Preventing Youth Violence Through Research- Guided Intervention." In: Trickett PK, Schellenbach C, editors. *Violence Against Children in the Family and the Community.* Washington, DC: American Psychological Association, 1998: 371-399.

Slaby RG. "Psychological Mediators of Violence in Urban Youth." In: McCord J, editor. *Violence and Childhood in the Inner City.* New York: Cambridge University Press, 1997.

Slaby RG, Roedell W, Arezzo E, Hendrix K. *Early Violence Prevention: Tools for Teachers of Young Children.* Washington, DC: National Association for the Education of Young Children, 1995.

Wiist WH, Jackson RH, Jackson KW. "Peer and Community Leader Education to Prevent Youth Violence." *American Journal of Preventive Medicine* 1996;12(5 suppl):56-64.

Yung BR, Hammond WR. *Evaluation and Activity Report: Positive Adolescent Choices Training Program,* 1993. Final grant report to the Ohio Governor's Office of Criminal Justice Services: 92-DG-BO1-7138.

Yung BR, Hammond WR. *PACT. Positive Adolescent Choices Training: A Model for Violence Prevention Groups with African- American Youth. Program Guide.* Champaign, IL: Research Press, 1995.

Yung BR, Hammond WR. "Breaking the Cycle: A Culturally Sensitive Violence Prevention Program for African-American Children and Adolescents." In: Lutzker JR, editor. *Handbook of Child Abuse Research and Treatment.* New York: Plenum Publishers, 1998: 319-340.

ADDITIONAL RESOURCES

Publications

The publications listed here provide useful information for practitioners who are planning a social-cognitive intervention

American Psychological Association. *Violence and Youth: Psychology's Response.* **Washington, DC: American Psychological Association, 1993.** Summarizes a broad set of strategies developed by the APA's-Commission on Violence and Youth. Strategies are based on 50- years of research evidence and practical experience.-

American Psychological Association-
750 First St., NE Washington,
DC 20002-4242-
Phone: 202-336-5500-
Web site: www.apa.org/books-

Children's Safety Network. *Taking Action to Prevent Adolescent Violence: Educational Resources for Schools and Community Organizations.* **Newton, MA: Education Development Center, Inc., 1995.** Describes more than 80 violence prevention curricula and 150-videos.

Education Development Center, Inc.-
Children's Safety Network-

55 Chapel St. -
Newton, MA 02458-1060-
Phone: 617-969-7100-
Fax: 617-527-4096 -
E-mail: csn@edc.org-
Web site: www.edc.org/HHD/csn-

Eliott DS, series editor. *Blueprints for Violence Prevention. Book Ten: Promoting Alternative Thinking Strategies.* **Denver: C&M Press, 1998.** Describes in-depth 10 violence prevention interventions thatmeet research design and evaluation criteria and havedemonstrated significant deterrence effects.-

Center for the Study and Prevention of Violence-
Institute of Behavioral Science-
University of Colorado, Boulder-Campus Box 442-
Boulder, CO 80309-0442-
Phone: 303-492-8465-
Fax: 303-443-3297-
Web site: www.colorado.edu/cspv/blueprints/index.html-

Greenberg MT, Kusche CA. "Preventive Intervention for School-Age Deaf Children." *Journal of Deaf Studies and Deaf Education* **1998;3(1):49-63.** Examines the effectiveness of the PATHS curriculum on the social, cognitive, and behavioral status of elementary school-age deaf children.-

Haynie DL, Alexander C, Walters SR. "Considering a Decision-Making Approach to Youth Violence Prevention Programs." *Journal of School Health* **1997;67(5):165-70.** Focuses on enhancing decision-making skills as one approach to increasing adolescents' ability to manage interpersonal violence and examines data from a pilot study for insights about adolescents' ability to make decisions in situations of interpersonal conflict. Adolescents can be considered fairly skilled decision makers, and their unique perspective must be considered to develop effective intervention programs. -

Hudley CA. "Perceptions of Intentionality, Feelings of Anger, and Reactive Aggression." In Furlong M, Smith D, editors. *Anger, Hostility, and Aggression: Assessment, Prevention, and Intervention*

Strategies for Youth. **Brandon, VT: Clinical Psychology Publishing Co., 1994.** Children who display deviant levels of aggression in school have been found to manifest significantly higher rates of juvenile delinquency, poor overall school adjustment, greater-than average rates of school drop out, and higher-than-average rates of referral for clinical mental-health interventions. Attributions may be internal factors for human aggressive behavior.

Lochman JE, Lenhart LA. "Anger Coping Intervention for Aggressive Children: Conceptual Models and Outcome Effects." *Clinical Psychology Review* **1993;13:785-805.** Reviews social-cognitive models of children's aggressive behavior and cognitive-behavioral interventions based on these models.

McCord J, editor. *Violence and Childhood in the Inner City.* **Cambridge Criminology Series. New York: Cambridge University Press, 1997.** Authors consider why so much violence exists in U.S. cities, why some people become violent and others do not, and why violence is more prevalent in some areas. They also discuss how the urban environment affects childhood development, and they review intervention strategies.

Patterson GR, Reid JB, Dishion TJ. *A Social Interactional Approach IV: Antisocial Boys.* **(Volume 4 of a series produced by the Oregon Social Learning Center.) Eugene, OR: Castalia Publishing Company, 1992.** Discusses the Oregon Social Learning Center's theory of antisocial behavior and what can be done to help families change these problem behaviors. Also addressed are attendant problems in the areas of peer relations, school failure, self-esteem, and depression. Factors that change the context of family process are taken into account, such as low socioeconomic status and divorce.

Pepler D, Slaby RG. "Theoretical and Developmental Perspectives on Youth and Violence." In Eron LD, Gentry JH, Schlegel P, editors. *Reason to Hope: A Psychosocial Perspective on Violence and Youth.* **Washington, DC: American Psychological Association, 1994: 27-58.** This chapter reviews a variety of social-cognitive models, their theoretical foundations, and their applications to violence prevention.-

American Psychological Association-
750 First St., NE Washington,

DC 20002-4242-
Phone: 202-336-5500-
Web site: www.apa.org/books-

Powell KE, Hawkins DF, editors. "Youth Violence Prevention: Description and Baseline Data from 13 Evaluation Projects." *American Journal of Preventive Medicine* **1996;12(5 Suppl).** This special issue summarizes the following for 13 projects designed to reduce youth violence: background, underlying scientific theory, intervention activities, evaluation design, and selected baseline data. -

Slaby RG. "Violence Prevention: A Shared Strategy." In Miller S, Brodine J, Miller T, editors. *Safe by Design: Planning for Peaceful School Communities.* **Seattle, WA: Committee for Children, 1996.** Discusses how parents and educators can contribute to a national plan for preventing violence.-

Committee for Children-
2203 Airport Way, South, Suite 500-
Seattle, WA 98134-2027-
Phone: 800-634-4449 or 206-343-1223-
Fax: 206-343-1445-
E-mail: info@cfchildren.org-
Web site: www.cfchildren.org -

Slaby RG, Roedell W, Arezzo D, Hendrix K. *Early Violence Prevention: Tools for Teachers of Young Children.* **Washington, DC: National Association for the Education of Young Children, 1995.** This book offers practitioners the latest knowledge on effective teaching strategies for early violence prevention. Includes chapters on helping children with aggressive behavior patterns,- encouraging voluntary sharing, and teaching assertiveness skills.-

National Association for the Education of Young Children -
Attn: Resource Sales Department-
1509 16th St., NWWashington,
DC 20036-1426-
Phone: 202-232-8777 (ext. 604)-
800-424-2460 (ext. 604)
202-328-2604

Fax: 202-328-1846
E-mail: resource_sales@naeyc.org
Web site: www.naeyc.org/resources/catalog/order-info.htm

Slaby RG, Barham JE, Eron LE, Wilcox BL. "Policy Recommendations: Prevention and Treatment of Youth Violence." In Eron LD, Gentry JH, Schlegel P, editors. *Reason to Hope: A Psychosocial Perspective on Violence and Youth.* Washington, DC: American Psychological Association, 1994: 447-456. This chapter deals with the broad issues that policy makers need to consider in order to reduce youth violence in the U.S.-

American Psychological Association-
750 First St., NE Washington,
DC 20002-4242-
Phone: 202-336-5500-
Web site: www.apa.org/books-

Shapiro JP. "The Peacemakers Program: Friends Don't Let Friends Fight." *School Safety Update* 1999;December:6-7. Describes a multi-modal program for fourth- through eighth-- grade students that includes a remediation component for students with serious aggression problems and a focus on violence- related values. The program has been shown to reduce aggression- related disciplinary incidents, including suspensions.-

Jeremy P. Shapiro, Ph.D., Director-
Center for Research, Quality Improvement, and Training-
Applewood Centers, Inc.-
2525 East 22nd St.-
Cleveland, OH 44115-
Phone: 216-696-5800 (ext. 1144)-
Fax: 216-696-6592-
E-mail: jeremyshapiro@yahoo.com-

Trickett PK, Schellenbach CD, editors. *Violence Against Children in the Family and the Community.* Washington, DC: American Psychological Association, 1998. Brings together the latest findings from researchers on violence and identifies future research needs. Also describes promising interventions that have helped children already affected by violence and suggests strategies for preventing violence before it occurs.- American Psychological Association- 750 First St., NE Washington,

DC 20002-4242-
Phone: 202-336-5500-
Web site: www.apa.org/books-

The table on the following pages will help practitioners develop age-appropriate violence prevention curricula. It is reprinted with permission from:

Promoting Social and Emotional Learning: Guidelines for Educators. By Maurice J. Elias, Joseph E. Zins, Roger P.- Weissberg, Karin S. Frey, Mark T. Greenberg, Norris M.- Haynes, Rachael Kessler, Mary E. Schwab-Stone, Timothy P.- Shriver. Alexandria, VA: Association for Supervision and- Curriculum Development. pp. 133-138. Copyright ©1997- ASCD. All rights reserved.-

For a copy of the book, contact:

Association for Supervision and Curriculum Development-
1250 N. Pitt St.-
Alexandria, VA 22314-1453-
Phone: 800-933-2723 -
Fax: 703-299-8631-
Web site: www.ascd.org-

	Preschool/Early Elementary (K-2) School	Elementary/Intermediate	Middle School	High School
Personal				
Emotion	· Can appropriately express and manage fear, helplessness, anger, affection, excitement, enthusiasm, and disappointment · Can differentiate and label negative and positive emotions in self and others · Increasing tolerance for frustration	· Expressing feelings in positive ways · Controlling own anger · Labeling observed emotions · Harmonizing of others' feelings	· Self-aware and self-critical · Harmonizing of own feelings	All areas should be approached as integrative: · Listening and oral communication · Competence in reading, writing, and computation. · Personal managment: self-esteem, goal-setting/self-motivation · Learning to learn skills · Personal and moral evaluations of self, actions, behaviors · Beginning to focus on the future · Exploring meaning of one's life, life in general, transcendence · Taking care of self, recognizing consequences of risky behaviors (sexual activity, drug use), protecting self from negative consequences · Harmonizing of own and others' feelings · Adaptability: creative thinking and problem solving, especially in response to barriers/obstacles · Earning and budgeting money · Planning a career and preparing for adult role · Personal career development/goals—pride in work accomplished
Cognition	· Beginning to take a reflective perspective—role taking—What is the other seeing? What is the other feeling? What is the other thinking? What is the other intending? What is the other like? · Generating alternative possibilities for interpersonal actions · Emphasis on attention-sustaining skills, recall and linkage of material, verbalization of coping and problem-solving strategies used	· Knowing about healthy foods and exercising · Times when cooperation, planning are seen; at times, shows knowledge that there is more than one way to solve a problem · Setting goals, anticipating consequences, working to overcome obstacles · Focusing on strengths of self and others · Ability to think through problem situations and anticipate occurrences	· Recognizing the importance of alcohol and other drug abuse and prevention · Establishing norms for health · Setting realistic short-term goals · Seeing both sides of issues, disputes, arguments · Comparing abilities to others, self, or normative standards; abilities considered in light of others' reactions · Acknowledging the importance of self-statements and self-rewards	

Personal	Preschool/Early Elementary (K–2) School	Elementary/Intermediate	Middle School	High School
Behavior	· Learning self-management (e.g., when waiting one's turn; when entering and leaving classrooms at the start and end of the day and other transition times; when working on something in a group or alone); · Learning social norms about appearance (e.g. washing face or hair, brushing teeth); · Recognizing dangers to health and safety (e.g., crossing street, electrical sockets, pills that look like candy); · Being physically healthy—adequate nutrition; screenings to identify visual, hearing, language problems	· Understanding safety issues such as interviewing people at the door when home alone; saying no to strangers on the phone or in person; · Managing time; · Showing respect for others; · Can ask for, give, and receive help; · Negotiating disputes, de-escalating conflicts; · Admitting mistakes; apologizing when appropriate	· Initiating own activities; · Emerging leadership skills	
Integration	· Integrating feeling and thinking with language, replacing or complementing that which can be expressed only in action, image, or affectivity; · Differentiating the emotions, needs, and feelings of different people in different contexts—if not spontaneously, then in response to adult prompting and assistance; · Recognizing and resisting inappropriate touching; sexual behaviors	· Ability to calm self down when upset and to verbalize what happened and how one is feeling differently; · Encouraging perspective taking and empathic identification with others; · Learning strategies for coping with, communicating about, and managing strong feelings	· Being aware of sexual factors, recognizing and accepting body changes, recognizing and resisting inappropriate sexual behaviors; · Developing skills for analyzing stressful social situations; identifying feelings, goals, carrying out requests and refusal skills	
Key concepts	honesty, fairness, trust, hope, confidence, keeping promises, empathy	initiative, purpose, goals, justice, fairness, friendship, equity, dependability, pride, creativity	democracy, pioneering, importance of the environment (spaceship Earth, earth as habitat, ecological environment, global interdependence, ecosystems), perfection and imperfection, prejudice, freedom, citizenship, liberty, home, industriousness, continuity, competence	relationships, healthy relationships, fidelity, intimacy, love, responsibility, commitment, respect, love and loss, caring, knowledge, growth, human commonalities, work/workplace, emotional intelligence, spirituality, ideas, inventions, identity, self-awareness

	Preschool/Early Elementary (K–2) School	Elementary/Intermediate	Middle School	High School
Peers/Social	· Being a member of a group: sharing, listening, taking turns, cooperating, negotiating disputes, being considerate and helpful · Initiating interactions · Can resolve conflict without fighting; compromising · Understands justifiable self-defense · Empathetic toward peers: showing emotional distress when others are suffering; developing a sense of helping rather than hurting or neglecting; respecting rather than belittling, and supporting and protecting rather than dominating others; awareness of the thoughts, feelings, and experiences of others (perspective taking)	· Listening carefully · Conducting a reciprocal conversation · Using tone of voice, eye contact, posture, and language appropriate to peers (and adults) · Skills for making friends, entering peer groups—can judge peers' feelings, thoughts, plans, actions · Learning to include and exclude others · Expanding peer groups · Friendships based on mutual trust and assistance · Shows altruistic behavior among friends · Becoming assertive, self-calming, cooperative · Learning to cope with peer pressure to conform (e.g., dress) · Learning to set boundaries, to deal with secrets · Dealing positively with rejection	· Choosing friends thoughtfully but aware of group norms, popular trends · Developing peer leadership skills · Dealing with conflict among friends · Recognizing and accepting alternatives to aggression and violence · Belonging is recognized as very important	· Effective behavior in peer groups · Peer leadership/responsible membership · Using request and refusal skills · Initiating and maintaining cross-gender friends and romantic relationships · Understanding responsible behavior at social events · Dealing with drinking and driving

	Preschool/Early Elementary (K-2) School	Elementary/Intermediate	Middle School	High School
Family	· Being a family member: being considerate and helpful, expressing caring, and developing capacity for intimacy · Making contributions at home—chores, responsibilities · Relating to siblings—sharing, taking turns, initiating interactions, negotiating disputes, helping, caring · Internalizing values modelled in family · Self-confident and trusting—what they can expect from adults; believe that they are important; that their needs and wishes matter; that they can succeed; that they can trust their caregivers; that adults can be helpful · Intellectually inquisitive—like to explore their home and the world around them · Homes (and communities) free from violence · Home life includes consistent, stimulating contact with caring adults	· Understanding different family forms and structures · Cooperating around household tasks · Acknowledging compliments · Valuing own uniqueness as individual and as family contributor · Sustaining positive interactions with parents and other adult relatives, friends · Showing affection, negative feelings appropriately · Being close, establishing intimacy and boundaries · Accepting failure/difficulty and continuing effort	· Recognizing conflict between parents' and peers' values (e.g., dress, importance of achievement) · Learning about stages in adults' and parents' lives · Valuing of rituals	· Becoming independent · Talking with parents about daily activities, learning self-disclosure skills · Preparing for parenting, family responsibilities

School-Related	Preschool/Early Elementary (K-2) Early School	Elementary/Intermediate	Middle School	High School
Reasonable Expectations	• Paying attention to teachers • Understanding similarities and differences (e.g. skin color, physical disabilities) • Working to the best of one's ability • Using words effectively, especially for feelings • Cooperating • Responding positively to approval • Thinking out loud, asking questions • Expressing self in art, music games, dramatic play • Likes starting more than finishing • Deriving security in repetition, routines • Able to articulate likes and dislikes, has clear sense of strengths, areas of mastery, can articulate these, and has opportunities to engage in these • Exploring the environment • Self-confident and trusting—what they can expect from adults in the school; believing that they are important; that their needs and wishes matter; that they can succeed; that they can trust adults in school; that adults in school can be helpful	• Setting academic goals, planning study time, completing assignments • Learning to work on teams • Accepting similarities and differences (e.g. appearance, ability levels) • Cooperating, helping—especially younger children • Bouncing back from mistakes • Able to work hard on projects • Beginning, carrying through on, and completing tasks • Good problem solving • Forgiving after anger • Generally truthful • Showing pride in accomplishments • Can calm down after being upset, losing one's temper, or crying • Able to follow directions for school tasks, routines • Carrying out commitments to classmates, teachers • Showing appropriate helpfulness • Knowing how to ask for help • Refusing negative peer pressure	• Will best accept modified rules • Enjoys novelty over repetition • Can learn planning and management skills to complete school requirements	• Making a realistic academic plan, recognizing personal strengths, persisting to achieve goals in spite of setbacks • Planning a career/post-high school pathways • Group effectiveness: interpersonal skills, negotiation, teamwork • Organizational effectiveness and leadership—making a contribution to classroom and school

	Preschool/Early Elementary (K-2) School	Elementary/Intermediate	Middle School	High School
Appropriate Environment	· Clear classroom, school rules · Opportunities for responsibility in the classroom · Authority clear, fair, deserving of respect · Frequent teacher redirection · Classrooms and school-related locations free from violence and threat · School life includes consistent, stimulating contact with caring adults	· Opportunities to comfort peer or classmate in distress, help new persons feel accepted/included · Being in groups, group activities · Making/using effective group rules · Participating in story-based learning · Opportunities to negotiate · Time for laughter, occasional silliness	· Minimizing lecture-mode of instruction · Varying types of student products (deemphasize written reports) · Opportunities to participate in setting policy · Clear expectations about truancy, substance use, violent behavior · Opportunities for setting, reviewing personal norms/standards · Group/academic/extracurricular memberships	· Guidance/structure for goal setting, future planning, post-school transition (future planning, post-school transition · Opportunities for participating in school service and other nonacademic involvement · Being a role model for younger students
Community	· Curiosity about how and why things happen · Recognizing a pluralistic society (e.g. aware of holidays, customs, cultural groups) · Accepting responsibility for the environment · Participating in community events (e.g. religious observances, recycling)	· Joining groups outside the school · Learning about, accepting cultural, community differences · Helping people in need	· Understanding and accepting differences in one's community · Identifying and resisting negative group influences · Developing involvements in community projects · Apprenticing/training for leadership roles	· Contributing to community service or environmental projects · Accepting responsibility for the environment · Understanding elements of employment · Understanding issues of government
Events Triggering Preventive Services	· Coping with divorce · Dealing with death in the family · Becoming a big brother or big sister · Dealing with family moves	· Coping with divorce · Dealing with death in the family · Becoming a big brother or big sister · Dealing with family moves	· Coping with divorce · Dealing with death in the family · Dealing with a classmate's drug use or delinquent behavior	· Coping with divorce · Dealing with death in the family · Dealing with a classmate's drug use or delinquent behavior; injury or death due to violence, pregnancy, suicide, HIV/AIDS · Transition from high school to workplace, college, living away from home

MENTORING STRATEGY

The presence of a positive adult role model to supervise and guide a child's behavior is a key protective factor against violence.

Overview of the Mentoring Strategy

Research has shown that the presence of a positive adult role model to supervise and guide a child's behavior is a key protective factor against violence (National Resource Center 1999). The absence of such a role model—whether a parent or other individual—has been linked to a child's risk for drug and alcohol use, sexual promiscuity, aggressive or violent behavior, and inability to maintain stable employment later in life (Beier et al. 2000; Walker and Freedman 1996).

Mentoring—the pairing of a young person with a volunteer who acts as a supportive, nonjudgmental role model—has been touted by many as an excellent means of providing a child or adolescent with a positive adult influence when such an influence does not otherwise exist (Council 1996; Brewer et al. 1995). Evidence has shown that mentoring can significantly improve school attendance and performance, reduce violent behavior, decrease the likelihood of drug use, and improve relationships with friends and parents (Sipe 1996). And the Council on Crime in America (1997) identified mentoring as one of three interlocking crime-prevention strategies (the other two—monitoring and ministering1—also provide adult contact).

Best Practices of Mentoring Interventions

Many states and cities, community organizations, fraternities and sororities, professional associations, and schools have launched mentoring efforts in the past decade or two. Anecdotal information from these endeavors has indicated that mentoring can be effective in reducing negative behaviors and associated risk factors. However, structured evaluation of mentoring interventions has only recently begun. And although violence prevention is one of many positive results that can come from the relationships formed through mentoring, few interventions have focused on that outcome specifically. Some researchers note that reliable data about how and why mentoring works is still being developed, but some commonsense wisdom about the best practices for both mentors and programs has emerged (Freedman 1993). Those practices, gleaned from an extensive literature review and consultation with experts in the field of youth violence prevention, are presented here.

Identify the Populations You Want to Reach

Most mentoring efforts target young people at risk for academic and social problems. In a survey of 722 mentoring programs (Sipe and Roder 1999), the majority of interventions were aimed at youths in need of adult role models; often, this status was defined as children from single-parent homes. Other common participant groups were children from low-income families; youths who had been identified as lacking self-esteem or social skills; young victims of abuse or neglect; and young people whose family members abused drugs or alcohol. To determine whom to target in your community, conduct a needs assessment, consider your resources, and consult with local leaders, policy makers, teachers, and community organizations that serve children.

Keep in mind that mentoring may not be viable for the children and adolescents at highest risk, as these populations typically require efforts that begin at a very young age and last for many years (Freedman 1993). Weigh the costs and benefits of engaging children and adolescents with severe behavioral or emotional problems—such as those who have attempted suicide, use drugs, or are in a position to harm themselves or others—in mentoring programs, and determine if other interventions might be more appropriate. Also, because successful mentoring depends on a long-term relationship, avoid targeting young people from whom there is a demonstrated lack of commitment.

> *Mentoring interventions can be community-based or site-based.*

Consider the Cultural and Demographic Context of Intended Participants

In most cases, mentors' backgrounds will be significantly different from those of participants in terms of age, lifestyle, ethnicity, and class. Mentoring efforts must take those differences into account and develop activities and techniques for bridging gaps. These interventions must also recognize the power of other influences in the lives of disadvantaged youths, such as poverty, exposure to violence, and lack of parental supervision. For many at-risk young people, mentoring is just a "drop in the bucket."

Select an Appropriate Setting

Mentoring interventions can be community-based or site-based. The setting should be determined by an intervention's goals, the number of mentors, the number of youths you want to serve, and the types of activities planned.

Community-Based Mentoring

In a community-based intervention, there is no set location where sessions must occur; the venue may vary by mentor mentee pair and by session. In Sipe and Roder's survey (1999), slightly more than half of the programs were community-based. The majority of these interventions featured one-on-one sessions between mentors and mentees, and many focused on social or recreational activities. Because the location can vary, community-based efforts often include field trips as part of their activities.

Big Brothers/Big Sisters (BB/BS), founded in 1904, is the oldest and best-known community-based mentoring intervention in the United States; it has also been studied most. Its mission is to provide young people with one-on-one relationships that help them develop according to their full potential and become confident, competent, and caring adults. There are more than 500 local BB/BS agencies in all 50 states, serving more than 100,000 youths. Mentor-mentee pairs meet one-on-one for three to five hours each week for at least one year. There are no prescribed activities—they may include taking a walk, watching TV, playing games, attending a movie or sporting event, visiting the library, or just sharing thoughts (Elliott 1997).

Public/Private Ventures (P/PV), a nonprofit social-policy development and evaluation firm in Philadelphia, conducted a comparative study of 959 adolescents ages 10 to 16 who applied to BB/BS interventions in 1992 and 1993.2 Half of these adolescents were randomly assigned to a treatment group, for which BB/BS matches were made or attempted; the other half were assigned to waiting lists. In the group matched with mentors, the pairs met about three times a month for an average of 12 months; each session lasted about four hours. The treatment and control groups were compared after 18 months to determine what effect one-on-one mentoring had on adolescents' antisocial activities, academic performance, attitudes and behaviors, relationships with family, relationships with friends, self-concept, and social and cultural enrichment.

The study findings, based on self-report data from baseline and follow-up interviews or on evaluation forms completed by agency staff, revealed that the BB/BS program can have a positive effect. Little Brothers and Little Sisters, especially minority adolescents, were less likely than youths in the control group to hit someone or to start using drugs or alcohol. They also had better school attendance, academic performance, and attitudes, and their relationships with parents and peers were better than those for controls. No statistically significant improvements were found in self-concept or in the number of social and cultural activities that participants took part in (Furano et al. 1993; Roaf, Tierney, and Hunte 1994; Morrow and Styles 1995; Tierney, Grossman, and Resch 1996).

Site-Based Mentoring

Site-based interventions have one particular location where all sessions take place. Most site-based efforts are implemented in schools, but they can also occur in workplaces, churches, community centers, detentions centers, and public housing neighborhoods. Group mentoring interventions with targeted activities—such as academic projects and career- or skill building exercises—are more likely to be site-based (Sipe and Roder 1999).

School-Based Mentoring

In school-based mentoring interventions, volunteers meet with children for an hour or two, once or twice a week on school grounds. In these efforts, mentors focus primarily on activities that build academic and social skills, but they also involve the children in fun activities.

The study was funded by the Pew Charitable Trusts, The Commonwealth Fund, the Lilly Endowment, and an anonymous donor. School-based mentoring programs are fairly new, and it is uncertain whether they work as effectively as "traditional" community-based efforts. But advocates of school-based mentoring have cited several potential advantages, including the following (Herrera 1999):

- They may appeal to volunteers who are reluctant or unable to commit to several hours each week, which is often required in a community-based mentoring program.
- Intervention staff may be better able to supervise and support mentors because they all meet at the same place.
- Teachers and school administrators can also help monitor the intervention's progress.
- Participating in a mentoring program may increase a young person's social standing with peers; having a mentor is often perceived as being "cool."

Another possible benefit of school-based programs is a decreased risk of false accusations of improper conduct. These programs are believed by some mentors—especially males—to be safer than community-based interventions because of the close supervision by teachers and administrators. This perception of safety may increase mentors' willingness to be paired with children of the opposite sex; this flexibility may allow schools to match a larger number of students with mentors (Herrera 1999). One of the better-known school-based interventions is the Norwalk Mentor Program. Its goal is to improve self-esteem, attitudes, and attendance of students at risk for behavior problems and poor academic performance. The intervention's director is employed by the Norwalk public schools. School-based teams of principals, social workers, guidance counselors, teachers, and nurses serve as in-school resources for mentors, and one individual—for example, a principal or social worker— handles administrative details. Volunteer mentors are recruited from local business and industry as well as from community organizations such as municipal agencies, local church groups, retired-teacher organizations, college alumni associations, and fraternal organizations. A liaison between mentors and the school is designated from each participating organization.

Mentors meet with their students on school grounds for at least one hour each week. Activities vary and may include talking, reading, playing a game, and taking part in physical recreation. For mentees in high school, mentoring sessions typically focus on career development, and meetings may occur at mentors' workplaces. Mentors are encouraged to keep in contact with students over the summer. Parents and guardians are invited to a series of evening workshops and luncheons at the school. Every student who completes high school receives a scholarship for post-secondary education, funded by participating companies through the Norwalk Mentor Scholarship Fund.

Evaluations completed by mentors and teachers after the program's first five years indicate that students benefit from the Norwalk program. As a result of mentoring relationships, 87 percent of students improved their school attendance, 92 percent improved self-confidence, and 96 percent showed greater cooperation in class. Almost all mentors (96 percent) described their relationships with students as excellent or good. And more than 90 percent of mentors and students continue their relationship through elementary and middle school years (Weinberger 1992a; 1992b). The intervention, which in 1992 had more than 800 mentors, was the winner of the 1993 President's Volunteer Action Award. It has been replicated in a number of other cities in the United States and Canada.

Institution-Based Mentoring

Supplementing traditional services with mentoring may be tempting for institutions that serve young people. However, institutions thinking about implementing a mentoring program must make sure they can dedicate adequate resources to operating that component. Existing staff rarely have enough time or preparation to train, supervise, or support mentors. Additionally, mentors' roles within the institution must be clearly defined so both volunteers and caseworkers understand how mentoring efforts fit with the youths' treatment plans (Mecartney, Styles, and Morrow 1994).

Involve Parents and the Community

Involvement of parents and the community is paramount to the success of mentoring interventions. Parents must accept and support the presence of mentors in their children's lives. And the community plays a key role by providing volunteers and an infrastructure to support the intervention overall.

Parents' Role

In almost all mentoring efforts, parents are involved at some level. Parental involvement may mean signing a consent form for the child's participation, referring the child to a social-services agency or organization, or taking part in activities along with the mentor and child (Sipe and Roder 1999; Herrera 1999).

> *Involvement of parents and the community is paramount to the success of mentoring interventions.*

Community Support

In order to get the human and financial resources needed to implement a mentoring intervention, you will need your community's support. You can establish this support by first demonstrating a need for your effort. Data about the problem of youth violence and about the potential benefits of mentoring should convince local leaders and policy makers. Also ask for input when developing the intervention's goals and operational plan; this should increase the community's sense of ownership in the effort (NMWG 1991). If your intervention is school-based, make sure you have the support of administrators and teachers (Herrera 1999).

Project RAISE (Raising Ambition Instills Self-Esteem), one of four components of the Baltimore Mentoring Partnership (BMP), is a good example of a program whose foundation rests on community support. Organizations—such as churches, universities, businesses, and fraternities—are recruited to sponsor RAISE interventions for seven years. They recruit mentors from their ranks and provide various other activities throughout the intervention. The goal of Project RAISE is to decrease the dropout rate and improve the life chances of students in inner-city public schools by improving students' self-esteem and school-related behavior and progress, reducing high-risk behaviors such as substance abuse and teen pregnancy, increasing graduation rates, and encouraging the pursuit of further education or training (Freedman 1993; NIJ 1994).

Evaluations of Project RAISE have revealed mixed results. According to BMP, graduation rates for RAISE students were about twice that of students in similar schools who did not participate in the intervention (NMP 2000). An independent evaluation of Project RAISE, which used comparison groups and statistical tests, found some positive results after two years of implementation: the intervention improved student attendance and report-card grades for English. However, most participants remained far below average for overall academic performance and were at risk of dropping out. Additionally, promotion rates and standardized test scores were not affected among students in the middle grades. The effects, though sizable, were not sufficient to neutralize the academic risks students exhibited upon entering the intervention (McPartland and Nettles 1991). The researchers found that the RAISE model was much more likely to show positive effects when one-on-one mentoring was strongly implemented. Program success was also affected by variations in how sponsoring organizations implemented the model and by the size and composition of the student group served (McPartland and Nettles 1991).

Set Clear Goals and Objectives for Intervention Outcomes and Implementation

Mentoring programs are extremely diverse, in terms of both activities and desired outcomes. Therefore, it is critical that these interventions have clearly stated goals and objectives. These objectives will guide planning decisions for such elements as the number of and qualifications for mentors, and they will provide benchmarks to guide implementation and evaluation. Goals should be set on two levels—the intended accomplishments both for the program as a whole and for individual mentoring sessions.

Intervention Goals

In most programs, the over-arching goal is to develop successful relationships between mentors and mentees. In Sipe and Roder's survey (1999), nearly three-quarters of mentoring programs had the general goal of positively impacting the young person's personal development. In many cases, that meant increasing self-esteem, developing positive values, improving conflict-resolution skills, increasing social skills, or improving relationships with family and peers. Other goals identified in that survey were promoting social responsibility and improving school performance, school behavior, and attitudes. About one-fifth of the programs had a goal of decreasing delinquent behavior among participants.

Individual Goals

The goals and objectives of individual mentoring sessions may differ significantly among pairs. Mentors should work with mentees and their families (and teachers, if appropriate) to determine desired accomplishments and the steps necessary to achieve them. Mentors may find it helpful to establish a growth plan for the mentee and to review it periodically, with both the mentee and his or her family. Setting a series of short-term goals can increase a mentee's confidence and keep him or her focused and enthusiastic (NWREL 1998). In a violence prevention program by Self Enhancement, Inc., for instance, mentors help students develop individual success plans at the beginning of the intervention. These plans, which outline what the students hope to achieve during mentoring sessions, are reviewed throughout the school year to make sure sessions are progressing as planned (Gabriel et al. 1996).

Goals should be set on two levels—the intended accomplishments both for the program as a whole and for individual mentoring sessions.

When setting individuals' goals, keep the following guidance in mind (Freedman 1993; Sipe 1996; Tierney, Grossman, and Resch 1995):

- The amount of input a mentee has in setting goals should vary with age—the older the child, the greater the input.
- Consider the values and religious beliefs the mentee is exposed to at home—do not try to instill values that may cause conflict between the mentee and his or her family.
- Be realistic—mentors can't eliminate all the risk factors young people face, but they can help young people achieve specific goals and learn how to deal effectively with negative situations.
- Shift goals as warranted by changes in the mentee's life.

Select Your Intervention and Develop Appropriate Activities

The variety of activities that can make up a mentoring intervention is nearly infinite. The activities you choose will depend on the intervention's goals, setting (whether community or site-based), and format (one-on-one versus group); the mentees' needs and characteristics; and the mentors' experience and commitment levels. Table 7 lists some common activities, but it is by no means exhaustive (Sipe and Roder 1999; Herrera 1999).

Table 7 Mentoring Activities

Social talking about life experiences having lunch together visiting the mentors home	
	Event-related (field trips) camping or hiking attending a concert or an art exhibit
Recreational playing games or sports doing arts and crafts walking in the park going to the mall	attending a sporting event *Life skills-related* developing a fitness or nutrition plan attending a cooking class discussing proper etiquette
Academic working on homework visiting the library reading together working on the computer	participating in a public- speaking class *Job- or career-related* visiting the workplace developing a resume
Civic helping in a community clean-up effort working at a soup kitchen	talking about career options practicing interview skills

Keep the following guidance in mind when planning your activities (Freedman 1993; Sipe 1996):

- Make activities fun as well as educational.
- Focus on activities that promote mutual exchange, rather than on instruction for the mentee.
- Plan activities that offer challenges.
- Provide support and encouragement, but do not solve
- problems for the mentee.

Intervention Format

Most mentoring interventions have a one-on-one format. Usually, this format matches one mentor with one mentee. However, a mentor can also be matched with several mentees with whom he or she meets individually. The most common examples of the multiple one-on-one format are programs in which retired persons meet individually with several children each day of the week (Sipe and Roder 1999). The Friends of the Children program, based in Portland, Oregon, also uses this format. Their mentors—called "friends"—are paired with up to eight children with whom they meet individually several times a week (Woo 1999).

> *Make activities fun as well as educational. Practitioners must carefully balance the desire to achieve high staffing levels with the need to select staff members who are qualified, dedicated, and able to make a long-term commitment.*

Mentoring can also be done in a group setting. This format most often matches one mentor with a group of young people. The groups typically include about four or five children, but they can range from two to 20 or 30 youths. Some group programs match two or more mentors with a group of participants. Assigning multiple mentors to a group may have several advantages. It reduces the mentor-to-mentee ratio, allowing for more personal attention for mentees. It allows mentoring programs to reach greater numbers of young people. And it reduces the problems that occur when a mentor is unable to attend a session—if one mentor cannot attend, the group can still meet with the other mentor(s). We should note, however, that very little research has been done on group programs, so we do not know if this format produces effective relationships or if youths derive the same benefits from a group format that they do in a one-on-one program (Sipe and Roder 1999).

Building on Others' Experience

Identifying existing interventions on which to model your effort can prevent your having to reinvent the wheel. If you know of a mentoring program that had positive effects, try to replicate it. You may want to tailor an intervention to your community, but be cautious in changing key implementation elements, as you may alter the outcome. The *Additional Resources* section on page 194 may help you find ideas for your intervention.

Select Staff Appropriate for Your Intervention

Mentoring interventions typically require a large staff. Many volunteers are needed to serve as mentors, and administrative staff are needed to train and support the mentors. Practitioners must carefully balance the desire to achieve high staffing levels with the need to select staff members who are qualified, dedicated, and able to make a long-term commitment.

Recruiting Staff

Before you recruit volunteers or a paid staff, clearly define the qualifications required for each position. Indicate the skills and characteristics that mentors and other staff members should possess. Put in writing the specific types of activities to be performed and the time commitment expected (NWREL 1998). The Big Brothers/Big Sisters program, for instance, requires its professional case managers to screen applicants, make and supervise matches, and close matches when eligibility requirements are no longer met or either party can no longer participate fully in the mentoring relationship. They also advise mentors when difficult situations arise (Elliot 1997).

Decide where to look for potential staffers and volunteers. The required qualifications and the intervention's activities will help you determine where the best pool of candidates can be found. The following ideas may help you locate recruits (NWREL 1998; Sipe 1996; U.S. Dept. of Education 1996):

- Contact community-outreach offices at universities or high schools.
- Talk with the public-relations directors of local businesses or corporations.
- Distribute information through local nonprofit organizations.
- Ask radio and television stations to announce volunteer opportunities.
- Advertise in the newspaper or get a human interest story placed.

You can also work with organizations such as the American Association of Retired Persons (AARP), United Way, and the National Association for the Advancement of Colored People (NAACP) to recruit staff. This strategy may help you recruit populations you would otherwise have limited access to. It may also save resources that you can then use for more in-depth screening (Sipe 1996).

Corporate Involvement

Ask local businesses and corporations to support your program and help you recruit mentors. One common model of such a corporate partnership is the "adopt-a-school" program in which a business enlists employees as mentors (Herrera 1999).

Businesses may also provide facilities for mentoring activities or sponsor field trips. Even if employers do not want to participate directly, they may be willing to give employees time off for mentoring (NMWG 1991). This is a very valuable contribution, as it allows individuals to mentor without affecting their personal or family time. More people may be willing to volunteer under these circumstances.

A study conducted in North Carolina looked at the effectiveness of Supporting Adolescents with Guidance and Employment (SAGE), a community-based program that combined several components designed to prevent violence and other high-risk behavior among young African American males. SAGE included an eight-month African American Rites of Passage (ROP) program, developed by the Durham Business and Professional Chain and the Durham County Health Department; a six-week summer employment experience, sponsored by the City of Durham Employment and Training Office; and a 12-week Junior Achievement (JA)-style entrepreneurial experience, led by 16 Durham businessmen. Mentoring by successful African American business and civic professionals was a key element of the ROP program, which also included lessons in African American culture and history and training in manhood and conflict resolution (Ringwalt et al. 1996). Results from an evaluation of the SAGE program suggest that it can have a positive effect on violence-related behaviors and other health risk factors. Self-reports of study participants 18 months after the intervention indicated that SAGE participants carried a gun and sold illegal drugs less often than did participants in the second study group (summer jobs and JA only) or the control group. SAGE participants also experienced decreases in heavy drinking and injuring others with a weapon. At 30-month follow-up, positive effects were decreased, as is typical for prevention interventions. The authors note that the results of the study are limited, as decreases in violence and other risk behaviors were not observed at statistically significant levels (Flewelling et al. 1999).

Career Beginnings is another program with corporate involvement. It is a multifaceted school-to-work initiative that targets disadvantaged high-school juniors and seniors who have average academic and attendance records and demonstrate commitment and motivation. Mentors support students in exploring college and career options through educational workshops, career-specific training, and quality summer work experiences. They also help guide students through the college admissions process or through the process of finding full-time employment. A 1990 evaluation of Career Beginnings compared youths who responded to follow-up interviews at one and two years after assignment with either the intervention group or the control group.3 Researchers found that Career Beginnings participants had a slightly higher rate of attendance than the control group. Intervention participants also had higher levels of college enrollment and higher educational aspirations than non-participants receiving comparable amounts of education and job-related services (Cave and Quint 1990; U.S. Dept. of Education 1993).

Older Adults as Mentors

A survey of more than 700 mentoring programs found that approximately 5 percent recruited older adults and retirees as mentors (Sipe and Roder 1999). Evaluations have suggested that these intergenerational programs can produce positive, satisfying relationships that benefit both the youths and elders (Freedman 1988).

Across Ages is one program that pairs high-risk young people with older adult mentors. It is funded by the Center for Substance Abuse Prevention of the Substance Abuse and Mental Health Services Administration and is coordinated by Temple University's Center for Intergenerational Learning. Originally designed as a school-based intervention to prevent drug use, the program has been expanded to address a variety of risk factors. A three-year evaluation of Across Ages revealed that a program of classroom instruction and parent workshops was more effective in preventing drug use when combined with intergenerational mentoring than when implemented alone. While both the mentoring and non-mentoring groups were more likely after the intervention to respond appropriately to peers' offers of drugs or alcohol, students in the Across Ages group also had a greater sense of self-worth and well-being and had fewer feelings of sadness and loneliness (LoSciuto et al. 1996; Taylor et al. 1999). Because of its promise for reducing risk factors and promoting protective factors, Across Ages has been selected by the Center for Substance Abuse Prevention as a model to be replicated in several sites across the United States. Linking Lifetimes is another intergenerational mentoring program developed by Temple University's Center for Intergenerational Learning. A study conducted by Styles and Morrow (1992) examined the relationships that formed between youths and their mentors at four Linking Lifetimes demonstration sites. The mentees in the programs were youth offenders, teen mothers, and youths living in high-risk neighborhoods. They ranged in age from 12 to 17 years; mentors were 55 years and older. Of the 26 pairs studied, 17 were identified as being satisfied with the relationship. Specifically, members of satisfied pairs indicated that they had feelings of attachment, fondness, and commonality with one another; they felt committed to the relationship and wanted it to continue. Additionally, satisfied youths stated that they felt their mentor was a source of support. Satisfied mentors felt appreciated or believed they made a difference in their youths' lives. It is not clear from this study, however, whether the Linking Lifetimes program had an impact on youths' behaviors or attitudes.

> *Intergenerational programs can produce positive, satisfying relationships that benefit both the youths and elders. It takes a special person to be a mentor practitioners must remember that mentoring is not suited for all volunteers.*

Criteria for Staff and Mentors

Mentors provide positive guidance and serve as role models. They act as teachers, confidants, friends, advocates, nurturers, and challengers. They devote many hours to their mentees and form lasting relationships with them. Clearly, it takes a special person to be a mentor, and practitioners must remember that mentoring is not suited for all volunteers. Other roles—such as support staff, tutors, or fundraisers—may be found for volunteers who do not have the qualifications or time needed for mentoring (Freedman 1993).

Although special criteria (to be discussed shortly) must be applied for mentors, all staff members—both volunteers and paid employees—should have the following qualities:

- belief in mentoring
- commitment to and understanding of intervention goals and values
- experience working with children and adolescents
- good organizational skills and attention to detail
- ability to work with people from different cultural backgrounds

Selecting mentors requires a great deal of forethought; being too lenient in your selection process can have very serious consequences. Develop written eligibility criteria to guide staff in making wise, objective selections. Above all else, you want to make sure there is nothing in an individual's past or about his or her character that would make that person unsuitable for mentoring. Red flags include:

- substance abuse problems
- history of child abuse, neglect, or molestation
- previous criminal conviction
- history of acting out or emotional instability
- evasion of child support
- interference with policies or procedures

You'll also want to consider practical matters and aspects of a potential mentor's character, such as—

- **Proximity to the mentee or the intervention site.** If a mentor lives far away, travel time may become an obstacle to regular meetings.
- **Age and other demographic characteristics.** Whether these factors are important will depend on your intervention activities and on your mentees' preferences.
- **Ability to meet regularly and make a long-term commitment.** It would be unwise, for instance, to accept a volunteer who travels frequently or is thinking about moving in a few months.
- **Compassion and tolerance.** Mentors must be caring and accepting of views and attitudes that differ from their own.
- **Desire to spend time with children.** Mentors should enjoy interacting with children and feel comfortable with youths who may be "cold" toward them at first.

Screening Mentors

There are several ways to find out if a candidate has the qualifications and qualities you desire in a mentor. The most common screening tools are written applications, face-to-face interviews, reference checks (both personal and employment), and criminal background checks (Sipe and Roder 1999). If the mentor will spend time alone with a child, you should also conduct home visits (NMWG 1991). If mentors are going to transport children, their driving records should be checked. And in some school-based programs, mentors must have proof of health requirements, such as a test for tuberculosis (Weinberger 1992b).

Train Staff and Mentors

The training required for intervention staff members will depend on their roles. For mentors, training content will depend on the activities to be conducted during mentoring sessions and the desired outcome of the overall intervention.

Training for Staff Members

The individuals you select to recruit and screen mentors should be trained in how to effectively approach organizations, corporations, and individuals about mentoring, as well as how to interview and screen candidates. Recruiters should also learn how to tactfully turn down interested persons without alienating them. Even though someone is ill-suited for mentoring, he or she may be an ideal candidate for a support position. Staffers selected to support mentors should be trained in maintaining enthusiasm among volunteers, developing creative activities for the youths, and resolving conflicts between volunteers and participants.

Mentor Training

Mentors should receive comprehensive training before being matched with mentees. Some general areas to address are the roles mentors are expected to play and the overall values, philosophy, and goals of the intervention. Specific areas to cover in training include the following (NMWG 1991; Styles and Morrow 1992; Freedman 1993; Gallup 1998; NWREL 1998; Herrera 1999):

> *Mentors should receive comprehensive training before being matched with mentees.*

> *Mentors must be patient and realize that the relationship will be one-sided initially.*

- **Trust.** An effective mentoring relationship is built on trust. Keys to gaining the trust of mentees include showing up for meetings and keeping promises.
- **Patience and perseverance.** Youths are likely to feel uncomfortable sharing intimate information. Some youths may be reluctant to talk about anything in the beginning. Mentors must be patient and realize that the relationship will be one-sided initially.
- **Communication skills.** Mentors must be able to share ideas with youths and suggest alternative behaviors and attitudes without

sounding like they are passing judgment. And they must listen intently to mentees, while watching their body language and picking up on other cues that might indicate hidden feelings. Good communication skills will help develop the relationship and set a good example for mentees on how to interact with others.

- **Problem-solving skills.** Mentees often face difficult social and academic problems. Mentors should be trained in how to help their young people come up with solutions.
- **Self-esteem building.** One of a mentor's roles is to help the mentee build self-esteem. Teach mentors how to guide their youths in setting initial goals that are attainable quickly and with relative ease. Early accomplishments will help mentees recognize their capabilities and develop pride in their achievements. As the relationship progresses, goals should become increasingly more challenging.
- **Developmental stages.** Mentors need to know about the developmental stages that children and adolescents go through. This will help them better understand mentees' behaviors and develop age-appropriate activities.
- **Cultural and economic issues.** Mentors should be informed about mentees' cultural and economic backgrounds so they can tailor activities to address the challenges mentees face in their families, neighborhoods, and schools. Because no two young people have identical backgrounds, some of this information should be provided to mentors individually when a match is made, rather than in a group training format.

Provide mentors with a training manual with a summary of material covered in training sessions, additional resources such as whom to contact for help with difficult situations (e.g., case managers or a program director), and suggestions for activities (e.g., lists of appropriate events and field trips). Also include guidelines on appropriate mentor behavior; procedures for handling emergency situations such as injuries; and policies for confidentiality and liability, which should include mandates for reporting physical or sexual abuse and other life-threatening situations.

Plan supplemental training sessions throughout the intervention and offer mentors retraining as their mentees grow into different developmental stages (for example, when the mentee enters middle or high school).

Resources for Training

Small sponsoring organizations may not be able to provide complete training. Identify sources of technical assistance for training; for example, partner with a larger organization or with a university.

Recruit Participants

Most mentoring programs are targeted to young people who lack positive adult role models or who have other risk factors for negative behaviors (Sipe and Roder 1999). But how do you find those young people? Sometimes they come to you. The Big Brothers/Big Sisters program, for example, has a waiting list and does not need to recruit. For most other programs, you'll need referrals from teachers or guidance counselors, community organizations that serve children, social service professionals, the local public housing authority, or the criminal justice system. You can also ask parents—through word of mouth or an organized communication campaign—to enroll their children in your program.

It is not enough, however, to simply locate children and adolescents in need. You must also make sure that the youths you recruit are going to be committed to the program. Make sure participants understand what will be expected of them. Also, make sure parents know what their child will be involved in and that they support participation. You can provide this information through—

- written statements, interviews, home visits, and phone calls;
- orientation meetings that describe the role of the mentor, mentee, and parents;
- a handbook for families and mentees.

Emphasize the opportunities for new and exciting experiences that mentoring presents.

Provide Incentives

Often, the experiences that mentoring relationships offer— improving academic performance, going to a movie, attending a sporting event, or simply having a trusted adult to rely on—are enough to interest young people in a mentoring program. However, if you are having difficulty recruiting intended participants, you may need to offer special incentives. For example, the Kansas City-based Ewing Marion Kauffman Foundation offered a monetary incentive to students who participated in Project Choice, a dropout-prevention program implemented in a local high school. If participants—who entered the program as freshmen—remained drug-free, avoided pregnancy, and completed high school on time, they received funds to cover their college tuition (Ewing Marion Kauffman Foundation 2000).

Focus on the Positive

Young people may be reluctant to take part in a mentoring program if it is positioned as an intervention or treatment for negative or problem behavior. Practitioners should emphasize the opportunities for new and exciting experiences that mentoring presents (NWREL 1998).

Implement Your Intervention

The success of a mentoring intervention depends largely on the development of trusting, beneficial relationships between young people and adults (or in some cases, older adolescents). To help foster this type of relationship, practitioners should remember three key principles.

First, both the amount and quality of time are important. Interactions between mentors and mentees must occur frequently enough to allow relationships to form. And mentors must be attentive to mentees during all interactions so they feel cared for and understood.

Second, sessions should occur regularly and consistently. Having a set schedule can help mentors improve their attendance rates (Tierney and Branch 1992) and give the young people something to look forward to. Sticking to the schedule helps build trust between the mentor and mentee. This point is extremely important—when a mentor misses meetings, the mentee may feel disappointed, angry, or let down (NMWG 1991). In a young person who is already at risk for academic problems, drug use, or violent behavior, these feelings can be highly destructive (Roder 1999).

> *Emphasize the opportunities for new and exciting experiences that mentoring presents.*

The Big Brothers/Big Sisters programs have taken race into account when matching their mentors with mentees. They have implemented a special campaign called "Pass It On" to recruit African American men. The campaign is based on the belief that same-race matching helps Little Brothers identify with their mentors (Milloy 1997).

The Juvenile Mentoring Program (JUMP), funded by the Department of Justice's Office on Juvenile Justice and Delinquency Prevention, considers gender when assigning matches. JUMP practitioners try to match mentors with youths of the same gender. In fact, almost all male mentors are matched with male youths. However, female mentors are matched with male youths about 20 percent of the time. This cross-gender matching occurs because there are many more female JUMP volunteers than there are male volunteers. Although agencies do not use race or ethnicity as criteria for matching, in nearly two- thirds of JUMP pairs, both members are from the same racial or ethnic group.

A full-scale evaluation of JUMP interventions is ongoing. However, a preliminary assessment based on grantees' feedback has shown that the majority of both youths and mentors are satisfied with their relationships. Additionally, both mentees and mentors believe their relationship had at least a little benefit in terms of improved academic performance and school attendance, prevention of drug and alcohol use, avoidance of fights, prevention of gang involvement, and improved family and peer relations. Slightly more than half of the youths believed that mentoring helped a lot in these risk areas; slightly more than one-third of the mentors believed their efforts had a lot of benefits (OJJDP 1998).

Cultural and Economic Background

Since one of the goals in a mentoring intervention is to provide youths with positive role models, it may be best to match young people with mentors from similar cultural or economic backgrounds (Freedman 1993; NWREL 1998). Mentees may respond better to mentors who can honestly say they have lived through—and overcome—the same obstacles the youths face.

Geographic Proximity and Compatible Schedules

Consider geographic proximity when matching youths with mentors. If members of the pair live near each other, they will be able to meet more easily and probably more frequently. Also remember that mentors and mentees must have compatible schedules in order for meetings to be regular and consistent.

Natural and Random Matching

Some practitioners let mentors and mentees form natural pairings. Workshops and social events allow mentors and participants to get to know one another and to develop their own matches. Another matching method is random assignment, in which no specific criteria are employed.

Match the Intervention's Frequency, Duration, and Intensity to Participants' Needs

Mentoring relationships develop through many interactions over a long period of time. Mentors should meet with their youths for an hour or more each week for at least six months, the minimum length of time typically needed to establish a close, trusting relationship (Freedman 1993; Sipe 1996). Sipe and Roder (1999) found that half of the mentoring interventions in their survey required a one-year commitment.

Some mentoring programs require mentors to commit to a much longer relationship. The Friends of the Children program in Portland, Oregon, is a mentoring program that pairs high-risk children with full-time, paid "friends" who commit to relationships that last for a child's entire school career. Friends candidates must be able to meet with their youths on a consistent basis over many years and must have a bachelor's degree and experience working with children. Each candidate undergoes extensive background checks before being gender-matched with up to eight young people. Being a "friend" is viewed as a career. All friends receive benefits, including insurance and a 401(k) plan, and a modest monthly expense account (Hallman 1999). Friends spend at least four hours each week with their children. Activities range from doing homework to going to the park or sharing dreams and ideas, but the overall goal of the activities is the same for all pairs—to teach problem-solving and conflict-resolution skills, honesty, respect for self and others, hard work, and accountability (Friends 1999a, 1999b).

Friends of the Children is in its seventh year, so final results are still several years off. However, the Northwestern Regional Educational Laboratory has conducted a preliminary assessment of the program, and results are encouraging. Their study found that having a mentoring friend can lead to increased self-esteem, better attitudes, and improved communication skills. Additionally, most participants improved their academic performance. In fact, only 2 percent of participants failed to pass their grade in school. Children in the Friends program also avoided contact with the juvenile justice system, and most

> *Mentoring relationships develop through many interactions over a long period of time. Interventions in which the staff contacts mentors regularly report better quality matches.*

Supervise and Support Mentors

Sustaining the involvement of mentors is hard work. Mentoring programs must provide ongoing supervision of and support for volunteers to ensure that meetings are taking place regularly and to prevent mentors from becoming discouraged or suffering burnout.

Interventions in which the staff contacts mentors regularly report better quality matches (Sipe 1996). Most programs contact mentors once a month by phone (Sipe and Roder 1999). Some programs institute monthly or bimonthly support meetings between mentors and staff, during which mentors can address concerns, frustrations, and difficulties. Other programs sponsor events such as picnics, parties, and conferences during which mentors receive gifts of appreciation, are recognized for jobs well done, and share success stories that illustrate how mentors are making a difference in young people's lives (Herrera 1999). When planning your intervention, develop an infrastructure that can adequately support the mentors. The median ratio of mentors to staff was 20 to 1 in Sipe and Roder's survey (1999). If most of the mentors in your intervention are inexperienced, you may need a larger number of support staff (NWREL 1998).

Encourage Continued Participation

The drop-out rate for mentoring interventions is fairly high. Some researchers have estimated that half of the relationships fail (Freedman 1993). Mentors must work to keep participants interested in the mentoring relationship. The following guidance for mentors can increase the likelihood that young people will stick with the program (Styles and Morrow 1993; Sipe 1996):

- Listen to the youths and respect their viewpoints.
- Involve mentees in deciding how to spend time together.
- Respect mentees' need for privacy; do not push them to share intimate information.
- Be available to talk at any time.
- Change strategies and goals as mentees get older; if necessary, change mentors to meet mentees'

Monitor Progress and the Quality of Implementation

As with any intervention, monitoring is necessary to make sure your mentoring intervention is being implemented as planned (NMWG 1991). Establish mechanisms to assess the progress of and satisfaction with relationships. These mechanisms can include—

- asking mentors and mentees to sign in for meetings;
- interviewing mentors, mentees, and parents;
- having mentors log activities, accomplishments, and concerns.

If you find that a mentor or youth is frequently missing meetings, follow up with that individual to see if there are transportation problems or time conflicts. If a match is not working, even after considerable effort by the mentor and staff, try to reassign both members of the pair (U.S. Dept. of Education 1996).

Evaluate Outcomes

When the intervention is complete, evaluate whether the overall goals and the goals of individual mentees have been met. Since one goal of any mentoring intervention is to form beneficial relationships, assess the quality of the relationships in your program. Determine how many relationships continued for the duration of the intervention, and ask both mentors and mentees how satisfied they were with their relationships. Another typical goal of mentoring is to prevent or improve some kind of negative behavior, such as violence, drug use, or poor academic performance. Ask parents and teachers to assess changes in mentees' behaviors; you can also ask the young people themselves to identify any changes in the ways they think or act. Other ways to check the impact of your intervention include assessing dropout rates and checking school detention and suspension records to see if disciplinary actions decreased during the intervention.

Remember to compare the behaviors, attitudes, and academic performance of young people in the mentoring intervention with youths who did not participate in mentoring (i.e., a comparison group) to determine the significance of changes. If, for example, all middle-school students improved school performance and reduced delinquent behaviors during the period of your intervention, you cannot assume that mentoring caused those changes in participants. They may have occurred without the intervention. Conversely, you may find that, although aggressive behaviors remained the same among participants, aggression increased among young people who did not take part in mentoring. Without a comparison group, you would not recognize the stable rate as significant.

*To have the greatest impact, mentoring should be part of
a concerted effort that involves several strategies.*

Maintain Results after Implementation

If your intervention achieved positive effects, you will, of course, want to sustain those effects. An important step in maintaining results is providing a supportive transition for mentees. This may be accomplished in a number of ways. Exit interviews between youths and staff, between mentors and staff, and between mentors and youths allow all three groups to discuss the benefits of the program and address concerns about what comes next for the youths. Recognition of mentees' accomplishments—through award ceremonies, banquets, and community or school newsletters—can motivate the young people to continue improving school performance, to avoid drugs or violence, and to seek out other positive relationships with adults.

It's helpful to link youths with other community services and activities, such as scouts and school or church groups, that can help fill any voids created by the end of their mentoring relationships. Assistance should be made available to mentees who have difficulty with the transition (NMWG 1991). Because some pairings may want to continue their relationship in some capacity after the intervention has ended, practitioners should have in place a policy for future contact. Make sure mentors understand any liability issues that may apply if contact continues outside of the intervention's auspices.

Link Mentoring with Other Strategies

The young people involved in mentoring interventions typically have several risk factors for adverse behaviors. Mentoring cannot overcome all of them—it is just one influence among many. To have the greatest impact, mentoring should be part of a concerted effort that involves several strategies, such as those discussed in previous sections of this sourcebook (Freedman 1993; Sipe 1996).

The Children at Risk (CAR) Program is a drug- and delinquency-prevention effort that combines strategies to offer comprehensive services for at-risk adolescents. These services include the assignment of case managers to participating families, tutoring and other educational activities, and police collaboration to reduce neighborhood crime. Mentoring is provided to about half of the youths in the program. Preliminary results of an outcome evaluation showed that, compared with a control group, CAR participants had almost half the number of contacts with the police and less than half the number of contacts with juvenile courts. A greater percentage of participants were promoted to the higher grade and had lower rates of chronic absenteeism. A full-scale case-control study is under way in high-risk neighborhoods in five cities to assess the effect of mentoring as well as intensive case management, family services, and educational incentives (Harrell 1996).

Summary

Although the mentoring strategy appears promising for preventing youth violence and many other problems facing our nation's young people, there is very little scientific data to demonstrate whether, and under what circumstances, it is effective. More rigorous and systematic evaluations are still needed. In addition, research must address several key issues (Sipe 1996).

First, we must develop more effective ways of recruiting and screening mentors. The largest mentoring program—Big Brothers/Big Sisters— supports 75,000 matches nationwide, but it has almost as many young people waiting to be matched. Fewer than half of the adults who inquired about volunteering during a study of Big Brothers/Big Sisters actually applied to be mentors. Of those, only about one-third successfully completed the screening and matching process; for some, the process took months.

Additionally, mentoring efforts have traditionally been targeted to children in the early- to mid-adolescent years. We must determine how to design effective mentoring programs for teens and pre-adolescent children, as well. Finally, there is little agreement about the financial resources needed to plan and implement a mentoring intervention. The Big Brothers/Big Sisters program estimates that it costs $1,000 to support a match for one year. But that cost may not be representative of all programs—researchers suspect the cost is somewhat less. In order to help communities assess the feasibility of mentoring, we must find a way to accurately estimate the costs of developing, supporting, and evaluating such an intervention.

REFERENCES

Beier SR, Rosenfeld WD, Spitalny KC, Zansky SM, Bontemp AN. "The Potential Role of an Adult Mentor in Influencing High-Risk Behavior in Adolescents." *Annals of Pediatrics and Adolescent Medicine* 2000;154(4):327-331.

Brewer DD, Hawkins JD, Catalano RF, Neckerman HJ. "Preventing Serious, Violent, and Chronic Offending: A Review of Evaluations of Selected Strategies in Childhood, Adolescence, and the Community." In: Howell

JC, Krisberg B, Hawkins JD, Wilson JJ, editors. *A Sourcebook: Serious, Violent, & Chronic Juvenile Offenders.* Thousand Oaks, CA: Sage Publications, Inc., 1995: 95.

Cave G, Quint J. *Career Beginnings Impact Evaluation: Findings from a Program for Disadvantaged High School Students.* New York: Manpower Demonstration Research Corporation, 1990. ERIC Number ED 325598.

Council on Crime in America. *The State of Violent Crime in America.* New York: Center for Civic Innovation of the Manhattan Institute, January 1996.

Council on Crime in America. *Preventing Crime, Saving Children: Monitoring, Mentoring, and Ministering—Second Report of the Council on Crime in America.* New York: Center for Civic Innovation of the Manhattan Institute, February 1997.

Elliot DS, editor. *Blueprints for Violence Prevention: Big Brothers/Big Sisters of America.* Boulder, CO: Center for the Study and Prevention of Violence, Institute of Behavioral Science, University of Colorado, 1997.

Ewing Marion Kauffman Foundation. *Project Choice.* Available at www.emkf.org/youth_development/programs/project_choice. Accessed June 13, 2000.

Flewelling R, Paschal MJ, Lissy K, Burrus B, Ringwalt C, Graham P, et al. *A Process and Outcome Evaluation of "Supporting Adolescents with Guidance and Employment (SAGE)": A Community-Based Violence Prevention Program for African American Male Adolescents.* Final Report for Grant No. U81/CCU408504-01, funded by the Centers for Disease Control and Prevention.

Freedman M. *The Kindness of Strangers: Adult Mentors, Urban Youth, and the New Volunteerism.* San Francisco: Jossey-Bass Inc. Publishers, 1993.

Freedman M. *Partners in Growth: Elder Mentors and At-Risk Youth.* Philadelphia: Public/Private Ventures, 1988. Summarized in: Sipe CL. *Mentoring: A Synthesis of P/PV's Research, 1988- 1995.* Philadelphia: Public/Private Ventures, 1996: 22-25.

Friends of the Children. *Unique Approach,* 1999. Available at www.friendstochildren.org/The_Program/Unique_Approach/ unique_approach.html. Accessed May 15, 2000.

Friends of the Children. *Who Is a Friend?* 1999. Available at www.friendstochildren.org/The_Program/Who_Is_A_Friend/ who_is_a_friend.html. Accessed May 15, 2000.

Furano K, Roaf PA, Styles MB, Branch AY. *Big Brothers/Big Sisters: A Study of Program Practice.* Philadelphia: Public/Private Ventures, 1993.

Gabriel RM, Hopson T, Haskins M, Powell KE. "Building Relationships and Resilience in the Prevention of Youth Violence." *American Journal of Preventive Medicine* 1996;12(5 Suppl):48-55. The Gallup Organization. *The Miracles of Mentoring: A Study of Mentoring for the 100 Black Men of America, Inc.* Princeton, NJ: The Gallup Organization, 1998.

Grossman JB, Garry EM. *Mentoring—A Proven Delinquency Prevention Strategy.* OJJDP Bulletin. Washington, DC: Office of Juvenile Justice and Delinquency Programs, U.S. Department of Justice, April 1997.

Hallman T. "The Pathfinder." *The Oregonian* 1999 July 11.

Harrell A. *Intervening with High-Risk Youth: Preliminary Findings from the Children At Risk Program.* National Institute of Justice Research Preview, April 1996. Available at www.ncjrs.org/txtfiles/high-risk.txt. Accessed June 2, 2000.

Herrera C. *School-Based Mentoring: A First Look into Its Potential.* Philadelphia: Public/Private Ventures, 1999.

LoSciuto L, Rajala AK, Townsend TN, Taylor AS. "An Outcome Evaluation of Across Ages: An Intergenerational Approach to Drug Prevention." *Journal of Adolescent Research* 1996;11(1):116-129.

McPartland JM, Nettles SM. "Using Community Adults as Advocates or Mentors for At-Risk Middle School Students: A Two-Year Evaluation of Project RAISE." *American Journal of Education* 1991;99(4):568-586.

Mecartney C, Styles MB, Morrow KV. *Findings from Two Pilot Programs.* Philadelphia: Public/Private Ventures, 1994. Summarized in: Sipe CL. *Mentoring: A Synthesis of P/PV's Research, 1988-95.* Philadelphia: Public/Private Ventures, 1996: 46-50.

Meyer W. "A Turn Down the Harbor with At-Risk Children." *Phi Delta Kappan* 1997;78(4):312-315. Milloy C. "In Search of Guiding Lights for Young Lives." *Washington Post* 1997 January 1. Reprinted in: *Nation's Cities Weekly* 1997;20(2):4.

Morrow KV, Styles MB. *Building Relationships with Youth in Program Settings: A Study of Big Brothers/Big Sisters.* Philadelphia: Public/Private Ventures, 1995.

National Institute of Justice (NIJ). Proceedings of the National Conference—Solving Youth Violence: Partnerships that Work; 1994 August 15-17; Washington (DC).

National Mentoring Partnership (NMP). "RAISE, Inc." *Programs*. Available at www.telementoring.org/programs/ raiseinc_man.html. Accessed May 30, 2000.

National Mentoring Working Group (NMWG). *Mentoring: Elements of Effective Practice*. Washington, DC: National Mentoring Partnership and United Way of America, 1991.

National Resource Center for Safe Schools. *Early Warning Signs and Resiliency Factors for School Violence: Resiliency Factors*. Fact Sheet Number 1, Spring 1999. Available at www.safetyzone.org/publications/fact2_article3.html. Accessed May 4, 2000.

Northwestern Regional Educational Laboratory. "Student Mentoring." *By Request...* 1998; September. Available at www.nwrel.org/request/sept98. Accessed May 4, 2000.

Office of Juvenile Justice and Delinquency Prevention (OJJDP). *Juvenile Mentoring Program: 1998 Report to Congress*. Washington, DC: U.S. Department of Justice, 1998.

Office of Juvenile Justice and Delinquency Prevention (OJJDP). *Juvenile Mentoring Program: Overview*. Available at http://ojjdp.ncjrs.org/jump/oview.html. Accessed June 2, 2000.

Ringwalt CL, Graham LA, Paschall MJ, Flewelling RL, Browne DC. "Supporting Adolescents with Guidance and Employment (SAGE)." *American Journal of Preventive Medicine* 1996;12(5 Suppl):31-38.

Roaf PA, Tierney JP, Hunte DEI. *Big Brothers/Big Sisters: A Study of Recruitment and Screening*. Philadelphia: Public/Private Ventures, 1994.

Sipe CL. *Mentoring: A Synthesis of P/PV's Research, 1988-95*. Philadelphia: Public/Private Ventures, 1996.

Sipe CL, Roder AE. *Mentoring School-Age Children: A Classification of Programs*. Philadelphia: Public/Private Ventures, 1999.

Styles MB, Morrow KV. *Understanding How Youth and Elders Form Relationships: A Study of Four Linking Lifetimes Programs*. Philadelphia: Public/Private Ventures, 1992. Summarized in: Sipe CL. *Mentoring: A Synthesis of P/PV's Research, 1988-95*. Philadelphia: Public/Private Ventures, 1996: 28-33.

Taylor AS, LoSciuto L, Fox M, Hilbert SM, Sonkowsky M. "The Mentoring Factor: Evaluation of the Across Ages Intergenerational Approach to Drug Abuse Prevention." *Child & Youth Services* 1999;20(1-2):77-99.

Tierney JP, Branch AY. *College Students as Mentors for At-Risk Youth: A Study of Six Campus Partners in Learning Programs.* Philadelphia: Public/Private Ventures, 1992. Summarized in:

Sipe CL. *Mentoring: A Synthesis of P/PV's Research, 1988-95.* Philadelphia: Public/Private Ventures, 1996: 38-41.

Tierney JP, Grossman JB, Resch NL. *Making a Difference: An Impact Study of Big Brothers/Big Sisters.* Philadelphia: Public/Private Ventures, 1996. U.S. Department of Education, Office of Research, Office of Educational Research and Improvement. *Mentoring.* Education Consumer Guide Series, no. 7, October 1993.

U.S. Department of Education. "Mentoring in Schools." *Creating Safe and Drug Free Schools: An Action Guide.* Washington, DC: U.S. Department of Education, 1996.

Walker G, Freedman M. "Social Change One on One: The New Mentoring Movement." *The American Prospect* 1996;12:75-81.

Weinberger SG. Fastback 333: *How to Start a Student Mentor Program.* Bloomington, IN: Phi Delta Kappa Educational Foundation, 1992.

Weinberger SG. The Mentor Handbook: *A Guide for Adult Volunteers, Sponsoring Companies or Organizations and Schools Involved in a One-to-One Mentor/Student Support Program. Second edition.* Norwalk, CT: Educational Resources Network, Inc., 1992.

Woo A. *Friends of the Children: Annual Evaluation Report (Executive Summary).* Portland, OR: Northwest Regional Educational Laboratory, 1999.

Additional Resources

Organizations and Their Products

The organizations that follow can provide a wealth of information about developing mentoring interventions. Many have publications and videos to guide you in planning and implementing this type of effort.

100 Black Men of America (BMOA)

A national alliance of leading African American men of business, industry, public affairs, and government who devote their combined skills and resources to confronting the challenges facing African American youths. Through BMOA's mentoring, education, anti-violence, and economic-development programs, volunteers in 82 chapters empower young people by helping them gain a competitive edge.

BMOA National Office
141 Auburn Ave.
Atlanta, GA 30303
Phone: 404-688-5100
Web site: www.100blackmen.org
Web link to local chapters: www.100blackmen.org/chapters.html

Baltimore Mentoring Partnership

A nonprofit organization with the goal of increasing quality mentoring opportunities for Maryland's young people.

Mentoring Resource Center
605 Eutaw St.
Baltimore, MD 21201
Phone: 410-685-8316
Fax: 410-752-5016

The following publications are available from the Baltimore Mentoring Partnership:

Mentoring Manual: A Guide to Program Development and Implementation. Manual for establishing, operating, and evaluating a mentoring intervention for disadvantaged youths. Published by the Abell Foundation, Inc. $10, Maryland residents; $25, others.

Partnership Mentoring Manual. Designed to assist school partnerships and others in developing and implementing mentoring interventions. Includes step-by-step instructions and sample forms. Developed in collaboration with the Baltimore City Public Schools and Greater Baltimore Committee. $5, Maryland residents; $10 others.

The Two of Us: A Handbook for Mentors. Designed to help mentors get the most from their mentoring relationship. Includes activities and ideas organized around seven themes. $25.

Big Brothers/Big Sisters of America

The oldest and largest mentoring intervention in the U.S., this national organization is a federation of 514 BB/BS agencies in all 50 States. They have served millions of children since 1904, primarily in mentoring relationships.

230 North 13th St.
Philadelphia, PA 19107
Phone: 215-567-7000
Fax: 215-567-0394
Web site: www.bbbsa.org
Available from BB/BS of America:

Big Brothers/Big Sisters of America Exemplary Efforts. Identifies outstanding advocacy efforts of 15 local BB/BS agencies.

Campus Compact

College-based community-service organization. Student volunteers establish or participate in programs to reduce racial tension, clean up the environment, work with the hungry and homeless, teach children to read, and much, much more.

Box 1975, Brown University
Providence, RI 02912
Phone: 401-863-1119
Fax: 401-863-3779
E-mail: campus@compact.org
Web site: www.compact.org
Available from Campus Compact:

Campus Partners in Learning: Resource Manual for Campus-Based Youth Mentoring Programs Provides resources and guidelines for college community-service organizations. Topics include orientation, training, planning an intervention, collaborating with schools and community groups, and evaluation. Also includes a resource guide.

Center for Intergenerational Learning (CIL)

Created in 1980 at Temple University, CIL serves as a resource for intergenerational programs. The center runs interventions such as Across Ages, provides training and technical assistance, maintains a resource library, and produces and disseminates materials.

1601 North Broad St., Room 206
Philadelphia, PA 19122
Phone: 215-204-6970
Web site: www.temple.edu/departments/CIL

The following products are available from CIL:

Across Ages Training Manual. Provides step-by-step direction for developing each component of the Across Ages program: (1) intergenerational mentoring, (2) community service, (3) a life-skills intervention, and (4) family activities. Includes program forms, evaluation materials, and training designs. $25.

Across Ages Video. Highlights the activities and interactions among participants for each of the Across Ages project components. Provides a picture of Across Ages "in action" and promotes the benefits of intergenerational learning. $25.

Elder Mentor Handbook. Resource for elder mentors. Includes child-development issues, suggested activities, and other relevant information. $25.

Elders as Mentors: A Training Program for Older Adults (with Facilitators' Guide). Ten-minute video presents typical mentor scenarios with vignettes that can be used separately in mentor training. Accompanying guide presents process questions and activities. $65.

Linking Lifetimes Program Development Manual. Guidance for developing intergenerational mentoring interventions. Includes intervention forms and evaluation materials. $75.

Linking Lifetimes, A National Intergenerational Mentoring Initiative. Developed to recruit older-adult mentors. This 12-minute video features mentor/youth pairs who share their experiences. $50.

Center for the Study and Prevention of Violence (CSPV)

CSPV provides assistance to professional groups committed to understanding and preventing violence, particularly youth violence. CSPV maintains a resource database and has developed blueprints for 10 exemplary violence prevention interventions, including Big Brothers/Big Sisters. Campus Box 442

University of Colorado
Boulder, CO 80309-0442
Phone: 303-492-1032
Web site: www.colorado.edu/cspv

Chicago Housing Authority (CHA)

CHA administers Project Peace, a school-based program that enlists 100 men and women to facilitate group discussions and participate in program activities; many of the volunteers become mentors. The program, which reaches about 1,400 students— most of whom live in public housing— combines the Violence Prevention Curriculum for Adolescents and a special intervention for youths at risk for violence. CHA Community Relations and Involvement Phone: 312-567-1831

Friends of the Children

Established in 1993 in Portland, Oregon, this organization serves 43 school communities and approximately 160 children throughout the Portland Metropolitan area. It provides a minimum 10-year commitment to each child, ages 6-7, selected for the program. "Friends" are full-time paid professionals who help children reach their unique potential.

44 NE Morris
Portland, OR 97202
Phone: 503-281-6633
Fax: 503-281-6819
Web site: www.friendstochildren.org

The Mentoring Center

Located in Oakland, California, the Mentoring Center provides technical assistance and training to organizations that wish to establish a mentoring intervention. Director Martin Jacks has developed a grid to help groups identify their intervention goals by characterizing interventions as "soft," "medium," "hard," or "hard-core," and identifying the types of youths and mentors best served by each approach.

1221 Preservation Park Way
Oakland, CA 94612-1216
Phone: 510-981-0427

Mentoring USA

Mentoring USA (MUSA), which evolved from Former First Lady Matilda Cuomo's New York State Mentoring Program, is a community- or site-based intervention that matches mentors with children in grades K through 8. MUSA mentors meet with youths one-on-one for at least four hours every month over the course of a year.

Stephen Menchini, Director
113 East 13th St.
New York, NY 10003
Phone: 212-253-1194
Fax: 212-253-1267
Web site: www.helpusa.org/mentoring/mentor.htm

The National Mentoring Partnership

(formerly One to One | The National Mentoring Partnership) The partnership
—designated by America's Promise: The Alliance for Youth to be its lead
partner for mentoring—brings together leaders from diverse sectors and
encourages them to recruit mentors, support existing mentoring
interventions, and begin new mentoring initiatives. There are currently 14
affiliates in cities nationwide. In addition to creating and sustaining
partnerships, the National Mentoring Partnership implements public
education and policy initiatives and develops and distributes products that
explain how to start a new mentoring intervention or expand an existing one.

1400 I St., NW, Suite 850
Washington, DC 20005
Phone: 202-729-4340
Fax: 202-729-4341
Web site: www.mentoring.org/f_resources.html

The publications that follow are available from the National Mentoring
Partnership:

ABCs of Mentoring Kit™. Guide to developing mentoring programs in the
    workplace. Includes video, manuals, templates, and recommendation for
    evaluation. $39.99.
Building Local Mentoring Partnerships. Learn how to rally community
    leaders to connect more young people with mentors. Free.
Mentoring: Elements of Effective Practice. Requirements and essentials for
    starting and maintaining a mentoring intervention. Free.
Mentor Training Curriculum. Comprehensive guide for training mentors.
    Includes training outlines and handouts. $29.95.
National Mentoring Technical Assistance Corps Directory. List of experts
    available to train and consult on developing, strengthening, or
    expanding mentoring interventions. $5.

Network of Mentoring Partners. A guide for information, connections, and consultation about mentoring through a national network. Free.

National Mentoring Partnership's Guide to Workplace Mentoring. Assists businesses in establishing school-based interventions. Includes case studies of workplace interventions and step-bystep instructions. $5.

National Mentoring Partnership Start Up: A Guide. Guides communities in developing a local One to One affiliate. Provides the start-up strategy for developing a Leadership Council, conducting a feasibility study, performing a needs assessment, and creating an operation plan for the first year. $100.

Select Mentoring Resources. A directory of materials on mentoring that are available from a variety of sources. Free.

Spirit of Excellence: A Manual for Mentoring and Tutoring African-American Children and Youth. Provides information on child development, discipline, encouragement, self-esteem building, and tutoring. Includes suggested reading lists for different age groups. $5.

Team Works Operations Manual and Team Works Trainers' Guide. Describes how to replicate a school-based intervention that creates teams of mentors and middle-school students. The trainers' guide includes all materials needed to conduct the intervention training.

National Organization of Concerned Black Men, Inc.

Founded in 1975 to help minority youth develop pride in their heritage while maximizing educational opportunities and promoting social consciousness and responsibility. Youth mentoring is among their programs.

1232 M St., NW
Washington, DC 20005
Phone: 888-395-7816
E-mail: glgjr@erols.com
Web site: www.libertynet.org/cbmno

Norwalk Mentor Program

Provides several products (listed below) that describe how to establish a school-based intervention.

Norwalk, Connecticut, Public Schools
125 East Ave.
Norwalk, CT 06852-6001
Phone: 203-854-4011

Connections from School to Career. A 48-page activity book for mentors to work on with their students in grades 7 through 12. $10.

The Mentor Handbook: A Guide for Adult Volunteers, Sponsoring Companies, or Organizations and Schools Involved in a One-to-One Mentor/Student Support Program. Written by Dr. Susan Weinberger, Director of the Norwalk Mentor Program, this practical booklet includes successful strategies for developing a school-based mentoring intervention. Also describes sample training programs, mentor roles and responsibilities, and student attributes and attitudes. $10.

Mirror Mirror on the Wall. A 48-page activity book for mentors to work on with their students in grades K through 7. $10.

Norwalk Mentor Program: Keeping Kids in School. Information packet describes the six-step process for beginning, maintaining, and evaluating the Norwalk Mentor Program and a school-based mentoring intervention. Includes checklists, sample forms, training guidelines, fundraising ideas, and news clips.

Q/A: Mentoring—Simple, Straightforward Answers to the Most Frequently Asked Questions About Student Mentor Programs. Booklet answers common questions about mentoring. $5.50

Office of Juvenile Justice and Delinquency Prevention

Offers an extensive database with information on juvenile justice issues, including mentoring interventions, through the Juvenile Justice Clearinghouse.

P.O. Box 6000
Rockville, MD 20849-6000
Phone: 800-638-8736
Fax: 301-519-5212
E-mail: askncjrs@ncjrs.org
Web site: www.ojjdp.ncjrs.org

The following publications are available from the Juvenile Justice Clearinghouse:

Guidelines for the Screening of Persons Working with Children, the Elderly, and Individuals with Disabilities in Need of Support. Covers the National Child Protection Act of 1993, state policies and legislation, and a three-part decision-making model to help organizations develop screening policies.

Mentoring: A Proven Delinquency Prevention Strategy. Provides an overview and evaluation of the Big Brother/Big Sisters program.

SafeFutures Marketing Toolkit. Mentoring is one of nine components of the OJJDP's SafeFutures Initiative, a multidisciplinary grant program to encourage more effective partnerships among health, mental health, child welfare, education, law enforcement, and judicial resources. This toolkit offers SafeFutures staff and planning boards the materials they need to effectively promote this innovative approach.

Points of Light Foundation

A nonpartisan, nonprofit organization devoted to promoting volunteerism. Their services include: assisting employers in developing workplace volunteer programs; participating in the development of youth service leaders and youth service programs; providing training and development for volunteer centers across the U.S.; providing products and services to volunteer management professionals; and aiding and encouraging the growth of the family volunteering concept.

1400 I St., NW, Suite 800
Washington, DC 20005
Phone: 202-729-8000
Fax: 202-729-8100
E-mail: volnet@pointsoflight.org
Web site: www.pointsoflight.org

The following publications available from the Points of Light Foundation's Catalog Service, 800-272-8306:

Church-Based Mentoring: A Program Manual for Mentoring Ministries. A how-to guide for beginning and structuring church-based mentoring interventions. $9.95.

Partnerships for Success: A Mentoring Program Manual. Provides guidelines for developing structured mentoring interventions in any organization. Developed by the United Way Volunteer and Community Initiatives Division. $19.95.

Points of Light Volunteer Marketplace Catalog. Catalog of publications, videos, audio cassettes, and promotional specialty items on volunteerism. Includes resources on program management. Free. Also available at www.mindshares.org/POLCatalog.

Prison Fellowship Ministries

A family of ministries that individually address each aspect of the crime problem. Among their outreach efforts is a faith-based mentoring program for youth offenders.

P.O. Box 17500
Washington, DC 20041-0500
Phone: 703-478-0100

Available from Prison Fellowship Ministries are the following products:

Alienation and Restoration: The Power of Mentoring. In this video, young people and mentors speak about their experiences with mentoring.

MatchPoint Leaders' Guide. Contains comprehensive information on mentoring relationships and provides a detailed method for training adults who mentor youth offenders or youths at risk of becoming offenders.

MatchPoint Operations Manual. Includes in-depth information on the ministry model as well as sample letters, assessments, case-management forms, and guidelines for operating a faith-based youth offender program.

Public/Private Ventures (P/PV)

Nonprofit corporation with expertise in policy development, research, technical assistance, and products for school-to-work initiatives. P/PV creates model policies, financing approaches, curricula, and training materials, and it provides technical expertise that can help implement new approaches more broadly, build staff capacity, and strengthen basic institutions involved in youth development. P/PV has conducted research on mentoring interventions and has published its results.

One Commerce Square
2005 Market St., Suite 900
Philadelphia PA 19103
Phone: 215-557-4400
Fax: 215-557-4469
Web site: www.ppv.org

A complete list of publications available from P/PV can be found on their web site. Included among the list is *Mentoring: A Synthesis of P/PV's*

Research, 1988-1995, a 76-page document summarizing major findings of P/PV's research and discussing the future of mentoring.

Save the Children
In cooperation with the National Mentoring Partnership and with funding from the Department of Justice, Save the Children has developed the National Mentoring Hotline, which houses a database of more than 1,500 mentoring interventions nationwide.

An ad campaign, produced in partnership with the Ad Council, was launched in the fall of 1998 to publicize the hotline and attract potential volunteers.

> Attn: Elizabeth Erickson
> 54 Wilton Road
> Westport, CT 06880
> Phone: 203-221-4257
> Hotline: 877-BE A MENTOR

YMCA of the USA
Interventions designed for at-risk youths are offered at 628 YMCAs; mentoring interventions are offered at 144. YMCA's web site has a link to help you find your local facility.

> 101 North Wacker Dr.
> Chicago, IL 60606
> Phone: 312-977-0031
> Web site: www.ymca.net

Additional Products

Beginning a Mentoring Program
Contains advice for launching a mentoring intervention, including tips on assessment, staffing, recruiting, matching, and funding. Includes sample forms. $5.

> WQED Pittsburgh
> Phone: 800-274-1307

Connections: Linking Youth with Caring Adults—A Guide to Mentoring

Provides information about building effective and lasting mentoring interventions. Outlines categories of mentor interventions, provides case studies, and highlights elements of quality programs.

Urban Strategies Council
Phone: 510-893-2404

Diversity in Mentoring

A video showing how interventions and mentors adapt to the needs of children they serve. Features four profiles of mentor- mentee relationships. $30.

WQED Video
Phone: 412-622-1300
Fax: 412-622-1488
E-mail: videosales@wqed.org

Faith-Based Mentoring: A Program Manual for Mentoring Ministries

A "how to" approach to beginning and implementing churchbased mentoring interventions, with recommendations drawn from actual interventions. Published by United Way of Southeastern Pennsylvania and One to One.

Church Mentoring Network
Phone: 215-223-8574

Guide to Mentoring Programs of Greater Los Angeles

Directory to interventions in the Los Angeles area.

One to One California
Phone: 213-627-0311

How to Start a Mentor Program

Based on the Norwalk Mentor Program, this 42-page booklet describes the six steps in setting up a mentoring intervention and includes sample forms. $1.25

Phi Delta Kappa International
408 N. Union St.
P.O. Box 789
Bloomington, IL 47402-0789
Phone: 800-766-1156
Fax: 812-339-0018
Web site: www.pdkintl.org

Mentoring Guide: A Complete Guide on How to Set Up a Mentorship Program

Prepared through the combined efforts of a variety of groups in San Diego. $7.

San Diego Consortium & Private Industry Council
1551 Fourth Ave., Suite 600
San Diego, CA 92101
Phone: 619-238-1445

The Mentoring Guidebook: A Practical Manual for Designing and Managing a Mentoring Program

Step-by-step instructions on how to start a generic mentoring intervention. $15.

National Dropout Prevention Center
Clemson University
209 Martin St.
Clemson, SC 29631-1555
Phone: 864-656-2599
Fax: 864-656-0136
E-mail: ndcp@clemson.edu
Web site: www.dropoutprevention.org

Mentoring in Schools

Includes eight steps for establishing mentoring interventions. Part of the Department of Education's *Creating Safe and Drug- free Schools: An Action Guide*.

Department of Education
Phone: 800-624-0100
Web site: www.ed.gov/offices/OESE/SDFS/actguid/mentor.html

The New Community Collaboration Manual
Step-by-step guide for building and sustaining collaborations within a community. $13.95.

The National Assembly
1319 F St., NW, Suite 601
Washington, DC 20004
Phone: 202-347-2080
Fax: 202-393-4517
Web site: www.nassembly.org/html/publications.html

Screening Volunteers to Prevent Child Sexual Abuse: A Community Guide for Youth Organizations
Information from the National Collaboration for Youth on policies for screening and selecting volunteers who work with children. $14.95.

The National Assembly
1319 F St., NW, Suite 601
Washington, DC 20004
Phone: 202-347-2080
Fax: 202-393-4517
Web site: www.nassembly.org/html/publications.html

Things to Consider in Starting a Volunteer Mentor Program
Provides a brief overview of issues to consider before starting a mentoring intervention.

Virginia Office of Volunteerism
Phone: 800-777-8293
E-mail: vol2@e-mail1.dss.state.va.us
web site: www.dss.state.va.us/program/volunteer/volunteer.shtml

Youth Mentoring Program Directory
Lists a sampling of national and local mentoring interventions. $5.

United Way of America
701 N. Fairfax St.
Alexandria, VA 22314-2045
Phone: 703-836-7112
Web site: www.unitedway.org

Youth Mentoring: Programs and Practices
Monograph on a variety of youth mentoring interventions. $8.

ERIC Clearinghouse on Urban Education
Box 40
Teachers College
Columbia University
New York, NY 10027
Phone: 800-601-4868
Web site: http://eric-web.tc.columbia.edu

APPENDIX A
A FACT SHEET ON YOUTH VIOLENCE

Support from community leaders, policy makers, funding organizations, and the public is key in developing and implementing a successful intervention to prevent youth violence. The first step in gaining this support is convincing stakeholders that youth violence is, in fact, a significant concern. On the following page, you'll find a fact sheet with a compelling overview of youth violence as a national public health problem.

Please feel free to copy and distribute the fact sheet. For more information about youth violence, violence in the schools, or firearm use among youth, please visit CDC's Division of Violence Prevention on the World Wide Web at www.cdc.gov/ncipc/dvp/dvp.htm and CDC's Division of Adolescent and School Health at www.cdc.gov/nccdphp/dash. For age- or sex-specific violence data or data for a particular state or region, visit WISQARS™, CDC's web-based interactive injury mortality data system: www.cdc.gov/ncipc/osp/data.htm.

Youth Violence—A National Problem

Violent injury and death disproportionately affect children, adolescents, and young adults in the United States. Although rates for homicides have dropped in recent years, they are still unacceptably high.

Fatal Violence
Homicide is the second leading cause of death among young people ages 15 to 19. Among African American youths in that age group, homicide

is the leading killer. From 1990 to 1999, nearly 34,000 young people ages 18 and younger were victims of homicide. That's an average of about 9 youths killed each day over the last decade.

Just as alarming as the number of young people dying from violence is the number of young people who are committing violent acts. In 1997, 1,700 youths under age 18 were implicated in 1,400 murders. Among the homicide offenders in 2000 whose age was know by authorities, approximately 48% were 24 or younger and 9% were younger than 18.

Nonfatal Violence

Violence does not have to be fatal to greatly affect individuals and communities. Violence-related injuries can leave emotional and physical scars that remain with victims long after the violent event has occurred. The rates of nonfatal victimization for rape, sexual assault, robbery, and aggravated assault are higher among people under age 25 than among other age groups.

Findings from the 1999 Youth Risk Behavior Survey (YRBS)—which is based on a nationally representative sample of students in grades 9 through 12—reveal that a significant portion of young people are involved in violent behavior. In the 30 days preceding the survey, weapon carrying was reported by 17.3 percent of students; 6.9 percent carried a weapon on school property. In the 12 months preceding the survey, 35.7 percent of students reported having been in a physical fight at least once and 4 percent reported being treated by a doctor or an average of nurse for injuries sustained in a physical fight.Almost 9 percent of students reported being hit, slapped, or physically hurt on purpose by a boyfriend or girlfriend during the previous 12 months.

Firearms and Youth

In 1999, firearm-related homicides were the second leading cause of injury death among 15- to 19-year-olds and the third leading cause of injury death among 10- to 14-year-olds. Nearly 25 percent of all Americans who died from firearm injuries in 1999 were between ages 15 and 24.

In 1999, about 1 in 20 students participating in the YRBS reported carrying a firearm at least once in the 30 days before the survey.Although this figure represents a decline since the 1995 YRBS, it is still troubling.

Deadly School Violence

Preliminary results from a current CDC study indicate that between July 1, 1994, and June 30, 1999, 253 violent deaths occurred on school property, on the way to or from school, or at or on the way to or from a school-sponsored event. The majority of these incidents were homicides involving firearms. These violent deaths occurred in communities of all sizes, locales, income levels, and racial and ethnic make-up.

Preliminary results also show that, while the number of school-associated violent death events has decreased steadily since the 1992–1993 school year, the occurrence of multiple-victim events—those with two or more deaths per event—appears to have increased. During the four school years from August 1995 through June 1999, there were 15 multiple-victim events; only three such events occurred between August 1992 and July 1995.

REFERENCES

Anderson M, Kaufman J, Simon TR, Barrios L, Paulozzi L, Ryan G, Hammond R, ModzeleskiW, Feucht T, Potter L. School-associated violent deaths in the United States, 1994–1999. *JAMA* 2001;286(21):2695-2702.

Federal Bureau of Investigation. Crime in the United States 2000. *Uniform Crime Reports*.Washington, DC: Federal Bureau of Investigation, 2000.

Hoyert DL, Kochanek KD, Murphy SL. *Deaths: Final Data for 1997.* National Vital Statistics Reports; 47, 19. Hyattsville, MD: National Center for Health Statistics, 1999.

Kann L, Kinchen SA, Williams BI, Ross JG, Lowry R, Grunbaum J, Kolbe LJ, et al.Youth Risk Behavior Surveillance—United States, 1999. *CDC Surveillance Summaries,* June 9, 2000. *MMWR 2000;*49(SS-5):40, 43, 46.

Snyder H, Sickmund M. *Juvenile Offenders and Victims: 1999 National Report.* Washington, DC: Office of Juvenile Justice and Delinquency Prevention, 1999.

Web-based Injury Statistics Query and Reporting System [online]. National Center for Injury Prevention and Control, Centers for Disease Control and Prevention (producer). Available from: www.cdc.gov/ncipc/ wisqars. Accessed May 28, 2002.

APPENDIX B
THE PUBLIC HEALTH APPROACH

The public health approach is a systematic process for identifying and describing a health problem, developing and evaluating interventions to prevent the problem, and implementing those interventions in communities. There are four basic steps to the public health approach. They may occur sequentially or, more commonly, simultaneously.

Step 1. Detect and define a problem through surveillance

Collecting and analyzing data allows us to identify a public health problem and to describe how big the problem is. In the case of youth violence, we would want to know how many people are injured or die as a result of violence committed by children and adolescents. We'd also want to know when and where youth violence occurs most often (for example, at night in public places or at home, immediately after school); characteristics of the individuals who commit violent acts (for example, their age, attitudes and beliefs, family history, school performance, etc.); and the circumstances surrounding that violence (for example, whether the perpetrator knew the victim).

And we'd youth violence cost society in terms of health care expenses and lost years of productivity.

The information gathered through surveillance allows decision makers to allocate resources where they are needed most. It can also tell us what kind of impact our efforts are having and whether we need to change course.

Step 2. Determine the causes of the problem

Studying the data on youth violence can help us identify risk factors that lead directly or indirectly to the problem. If we know who is most at risk for committing violence and why, we can develop more tailored—and, hence, more effective— interventions to prevent youth violence.

Step 3. Develop and test interventions for preventing the problem

The information obtained through surveillance and research helps us design interventions to combat the problem of youth violence. But before we implement these interventions on a wide scale, we need to know if they are effective.We must evaluate the interventions to make sure they work as intended, without any undesired effects. These evaluations may be conducted in a variety of ways: randomized controlled trials, controlled comparisons of populations for occurrence of health outcomes, time-series analyses of trends in multiple areas, or observational studies such as case-control studies.

Step 4. Implement the interventions

Once we know an intervention is effective, we need to share it with other communities so they can prevent youth violence. We can disseminate interventions widely through training and public awareness programs, through journals, or through special publications—like this sourcebook. [1]

Source: Mercy JA, Rosenberg ML, Powell KE, Broome CV, RoperWL. Public health policy for preventing violence. Health Affairs 12(1993):7-29.

ACKNOWLEDGMENTS

This sourcebook is the result of the dedicated efforts of hundreds of individuals. We thank the many practitioners and other experts who shared their wisdom with us in interviews and meetings, who spent hours reviewing literature review findings and draft manuscripts, and who helped shape the sourcebook's organization and content.

INDEX

D

E

F

J

K

L

P

S

sadness, 162
safety, 82, 83, 119, 123, 129, 154
sales, 70, 141
sample, 92, 179, 185, 187, 188, 189, 194
sampling, 191
satisfaction, 93, 125, 171
savings, 77
scholarship, 154
school, 1, 2, 4, 5, 6, 7, 9, 10, 11, 12, 13,
    17, 18, 24, 26, 27, 31, 33, 38, 39, 41,
    43, 44, 48, 50, 55, 56, 57, 64, 73, 76,
    77, 87, 111, 112, 113, 114, 115, 116,
    117, 118, 119, 120, 121, 122, 123,
    124, 125, 126, 127, 128, 129, 130,
    131, 139, 150, 152, 153, 154, 155,
    156, 157, 161, 162, 164, 166, 168,
    169, 170, 172, 173, 179, 180, 182,
    184, 185, 187, 193, 194, 195, 197
school activities, 12, 123, 127
school adjustment, 139
school community, 112, 123
school failure, 139
school performance, 73, 124, 157, 172,
    173, 197
secondary education, 154
selecting, 12, 39, 82, 191
self, 10, 40, 45, 46, 47, 52, 53, 63, 67,
    69, 72, 75, 82, 91, 115, 116, 117, 119,
    120, 121, 122, 123, 124, 130, 131,
    139, 151, 152, 154, 156, 162, 166,
    170, 184
self-concept, 45, 152, 153
self-control, 46, 117, 124
self-discipline, 47
self-efficacy, 91
self-esteem, 45, 63, 139, 151, 154, 156,
    166, 170, 184
self-report data, 119, 152
self-reports, 75, 116
self-understanding, 10, 121
self-worth, 162
sensitivity, 82

series, 48, 138, 139, 154, 157, 198
services, 17, 44, 48, 50, 54, 63, 64, 67,
    74, 78, 79, 80, 84, 85, 92, 94, 117,
    154, 155, 162, 173, 186
sex offenders, 79
sexual abuse, 166
sexuality, 42
shape, 7, 18, 19, 41, 199
shaping, 27
shares, 1
sharing, 87, 152, 165, 170
shoot, 1
siblings, 7, 48, 53, 64, 94
sign, 81, 82, 172
sites, 4, 68, 162
skills, 2, 7, 11, 20, 21, 22, 24, 27, 36, 43,
    44, 45, 48, 49, 51, 52, 53, 57, 64, 66,
    68, 69, 70, 71, 78, 79, 83, 84, 87, 95,
    109, 110, 111, 113, 114, 116, 118,
    119, 120, 121, 124, 125, 128, 138,
    140, 156, 158, 160, 163, 165, 166,
    170, 178, 181
skills training, 64, 70, 71, 118, 124
social behavior, 45, 46, 53, 115, 116,
    121, 122, 123, 129
social competence, 112, 113, 115, 123
social context, 123
social development, 120
social events, 169
social group, 27
social norms, 4
social problems, 151
social relations, 27, 110, 124
social relationships, 27, 110
social resources, 48
social responsibility, 157
social services, 13, 80, 93
social situations, 109, 110, 121
social skills, 10, 71, 110, 120, 151, 153,
    156
social standing, 49, 153
social status, 121, 125
social support, 44, 76, 78, 87
social workers, 20, 80, 81, 154